BELLEEK
Irish Porcelain

*An illustrated guide to over
two thousand pieces*

GIRL BASKET FLOWER CARRIER *(ST. 11) see page 10.*

BELLEEK
Irish Porcelain

*An illustrated guide to over
two thousand pieces*

MARION LANGHAM

Quiller Press

*To the two most important women in
my life, Thora Millway, my mother, and
Rosamond Lady Langham, my mother-in-law*

First published 1993
by Quiller Press Limited
46 Lillie Road
London SW6 1TN

ISBN 1-870948-77-7

Produced for Quiller Press by Hugh Tempest-Radford *Book Producers*
Designed by Chris McLeod
Typeset by Goodfellow & Egan, Cambridge
Printed in Hong Kong

Contents

BOY AND SWAN COMPORT. *From Roy Holihead's collection.*

Foreword

BY GEORGE G. MOORE

BACK in 1857, three great people came together and shared the vision of building and developing a world-renowned porcelain company. This vision included being a premier provider of fine parian china and earthenware, providing substantial employment in a traditionally depressed area, and operating on a sound financial basis. If Williams Armstrong, John Caldwell, and David McBirnie were alive today, I would be pleased to report to them that their vision is more than being realized and that their Pottery is facing great prospects. Belleek has withstood the test of time for 135 years, has survived world wars, civil wars, the Great Depression, and even our modern troubles. I am sure the road forward for the next 135 years will be less treacherous than the previous 135.

This new book by L.L is a great endorsement of the heritage and vitality of Belleek today. For all of you who cannot visit our Pottery, it gives you a grand tour through a pictorial exhibition of its history. I warmly thank and congratulate Lady Langham for her efforts. She has drawn together the worldwide lovers of Belleek and her book is testimony to the global joy that all of our Belleek friends share with each other. Additionally, Lady Langham's book records another period in Belleek's history and builds on the great works of dedicated friends such as Richard K. Deggenhardt and John B. Cunningham.

Being a transplanted Irishman in America, I have always wanted to develop and maintain a strong connection with Ireland; my family and I share a deep love for Ireland and my dream is for my children to maintain that deep love. The manifestation of this dream to establish solid roots in Ireland has been the purchase of Belleek in early 1990. Close friends and my family had prior associations with Belleek and it satisfied my conditions of being world renowned with a strong brand name, producing quality products, having a strong workforce, and being able to leverage my business skills. While the original purchase of Belleek was motivated by many influences, I quickly learned that Belleek has a soul to it. Our employees, collectors and customers have bred a living entity. I get greater satisfaction from Belleek than any of my other businesses and this satisfaction is continuously reinforced by our daily progress in restoring Belleek to its former glory as a worldwide quality porcelain company.

BELLEEK POTTERY STAFF, AUGUST 1992.

BELLEEK HALL OF FAMERS

1st
1986 CDR F B GARY
San Diego, California

2nd
1987 MRS M J WELECK
Chandler, Arizona

3rd
1988 PROF R E GREGG
Boulder, Colorado

4th
1989 MRS J CORRIVEAU
Manchester, New Hampshire

5th
1990 MR DON CLINTON
Los Angeles, California

6th
1991 MR E KRACH
Geln Arm, Maryland

THE STAKEHOLDERS OF BELLEEK

While Belleek shares a magnificent building, and has substantial assets, its real value lies in its stakeholders. These are the living assets of Belleek. They include our collectors, our customers, our distributors, our retailers, and, above all, our employee base.

Since the founding of The Belleek Collector's Society in 1979, we have gone from strength to strength with currently close to 6,000 members worldwide from Australia, India, U.S.A., Canada, and many European countries including the U.K. Nobody can accuse us of rushing into things by establishing the first Irish Belleek Collector's Society in 1991!

Our collectors form the backbone of our customer group.

They are all people who share a common love for a particular interest and act as global ambassadors for Belleek. Whilst every Belleek collector deserves our personal thanks, the geographical spread does not allow us that privilege. However, we can thank all these great people by recognizing the Belleek collectors who have been nominated to the Belleek Hall of Fame.

Each of these people have demonstrated excellence in their collection of Belleek and in their effort to provide a forum for Belleek in the Collector's Society.

Our general customer base is also a key stakeholder in the future of Belleek. Currently, we have 2,500 retail accounts in the U.S., 500 accounts in Ireland, 200 in the U.K., 200 in

BELLEEK POTTERY, VISITORS CENTRE.

Canada, 100 in Australia, and 250 in other countries. A core part of our strategy is to build a partnership with the retailer in order to effectively present Belleek to our loyal customer base. Worldwide, some of our key retailers include Harrods in London, Clerys in Dublin, Hoggs in Belfast, Macy's in New York, Pacific Rim Trading Partners in Hong Kong, Irish Design Shop in Sydney, Australia and Marshall Fields in Chicago.

While we have a solid distribution base worldwide, a key goal is to upgrade the image of Belleek with unique company-sponsored display systems and quality brochures and other collateral material.

A core part of our strategy in the U.S. market is our partnership with Reed & Barton, the renowned sterling silverware company. Founded in 1833, Reed & Barton are a little older than our own Belleek but they share our common vision for prestigious and quality tabletop products.

Another important stakeholder in our company are our visitors to the Pottery. Currently, we get close to 100,000 visitors annually; over 64,000 of these are from overseas and we

have totally upgraded the visiting facilities at Belleek to accommodate their wishes. The Belleek Visitors Centre has won many awards as a tourist destination point in the U.K. and Ireland.

The Visitors Centre comprises a museum, an audio-visual centre, a restaurant, and a major store where visitors can buy Belleek. As you can see, it provides our visitors with a wonderful experience and one that is memorable. Highlights of the Visitors Centre are the Belleek tours where visitors can take a guided tour around the Pottery and watch and talk to the craftsmen of Belleek. Our craftsmen get a particular joy out of this when the fruits of their labour are expressed with words of congratulation by our visitors. In fact, many of visitors are surprised at how Belleek is totally handcrafted; while many companies dependent on craft labour like Belleek have gone by the wayside, Belleek retains and will always retain its hand-crafted beauty.

The greatest stakeholders in our company are our employees. Many of our employees have been with Belleek over 40 years and have experienced all the ups and downs. Particularly, they have witnessed the treacherous period of the early 80's when the Pottery was almost closed down. They have weathered that storm and recognize the current and future vitality that Belleek brings to the community. Most of our employees live in the village of Belleek, population 800, and the very livelihood of the community depends on the prospects of the Pottery just as it did in 1857. Our employees take great pride in their work and the current good fortunes of Belleek are truly a function of their loyalty and dedication to producing high-quality parian china at affordable prices.

In terms of stakeholders, our employees are led by a management team. All of whom share a love for Belleek and recognize their responsibility for continuing its success. I am pleased to report that we have a very strong team all across the board including general management, design production, finance, personnel and sales and marketing.

The ultimate stakeholders in Belleek are the common stock shareholders. 100% of the ownership of Belleek Pottery rests with my immediate family. I truly believe that Belleek is a company that needs one major shareholder with one vision for its prospects and I am pleased to report to everyone that I hope Belleek is still in my family name in 100 years. My dream is that my children and their children and their children maintain the heritage and vitality of Belleek into the next century.

THE WAY FORWARD FOR BELLEEK

Companies like Belleek can go through chequered histories with new ownership and management but I am pleased to say that our business recipe for Belleek is working extremely well and all of our stakeholders believe that the continued execution of this recipe will result in a long-term financially viable life for Belleek Pottery. Key ingredients include:

1 Customer Focus   Our customers must always be the top of our organization chart and our reason for being. Our management, employees, and distributors start with our customers and work backwards to the product rather than vice versa. The Belleek collectors are instrumental in feedback to the Pottery along with our key retailers. We are planning to form Retail Advisory Groups of our key retailers to advise us on new product development and quality.

2 Quality   Our analysis shows that the quality of Belleek is greater than it has been at any time since the early 1980's. We continue to experiment with methods of making Belleek of the quality and eggshell translucency of former days. Quality will never be compromised; in fact, even today, we lose 25 percent of our production due to quality assurance procedures. Belleek sells no seconds and never will. While maintaining the total handcrafted nature of Belleek, we will and have introduced modern technologies to increase productivity, to ensure more

efficient quality control, and to maintain the affordability of Belleek. A major part of our quality is also expressed via the re-introduction of substantial pieces of Belleek from moulds originating in the 1860's. Current examples of this include the Chinese Dragon Tea Set, the Crouching Venus, and many other collector's pieces. All these pieces are created by a master craftsman using the original moulds as the base. The quality of these museum pieces underscores the overall quality of Belleek.

3 New Product Development   New product development is at the core of our strategy with 40% of the growth of Belleek coming from new products. While retaining the great heritage of parian manufacturing, our design team borrow from old and new to come up with contemporary products that appeal to our customer base today. Many of these products emphasize the tradition of Belleek with new baskets, vases, figurines, and teaware, but we also emphasize more utilitarian items such as clocks, photograph frames, and everyday-use teaware.

4 Respect for Employees   The original Belleek workforce was formed in early Victorian times and has witnessed the development of modern industrial relations. We are committed to the continued development of our people by providing a stimulating work environment with fair compensation levels.

5 Affordability   Though we have witnessed great inflation in Ireland and appreciation of currencies, our goal is to keep Belleek affordable for our customer base and to be competitive with alternatives for a Belleek gift. All of our stakeholders have greatly contributed to increasing efficiency and productivity at the Pottery and this translates into competitive prices for retailers and customers.

6 Strong Management   The leadership and vision driving any company must be infectious and strengthened by desire to build a significant enterprise for all stakeholders. Belleek today has strong long-term committed management with the ambition to develop Belleek to global prominence. The management team goes from strength to strength.

BELLEEK'S FUTURE

As of 1992, the major plans for Belleek include:

1 The Expansion of the Pottery   Though close to production capacity in our current premises, we have developed plans to expand and build a new Pottery connected to our main building. This will involve the removal of the current structures which are 1950's industrial style and do not provide the working environment that our employees and management deserve. While building a modern Pottery, we will retain the character of an old Pottery with window treatments for better lighting and comfort and modern work areas for employees. The new plant will also allow for touring where our visitors, after their long journey, can interact with our employees and gain a greater appreciation of the quality of Belleek. The project is currently in five stages to be started in 1992 with full completion in 1996.

2 Alternative Parian Products   While the focus of Belleek has always been 100% parian products, in the past few years we have experimented with different products that include parian as a major component. The Belleek Doll Collection is one-of-a-kind and brings together many handcrafted products from across all of Ireland including Carrickmacross lace, Irish seamstresses and painters. The dolls have been very well received as collectors' items worldwide and we will continue limited production to satisfy the requirements of our customers.

3 Belleek Crystal   Ireland also shares a great heritage for crystal manufacturing and Irish crystal is renowned and cherished worldwide. Just as Belleek breathes life into parian ware, we believe that Belleek's artistry can be expressed in the cuts of premium crystal.

It is also our strong belief that Belleek as an entity must be large to be strong in the future. We are currently experimenting with designs and production facilities and are working on a whole new line of Belleek Crystal.

Our strategy here parallels the Belleek Pottery parian strategy of quality and affordability with a strong customer focus.

Given that we are starting with blank paper, it is viable for Belleek to manufacture super premium crystal at very competitive prices and further enhance the great name of Belleek worldwide. This is a whole new phase and an exciting time for Belleek. We would hope that our collectors and retailers join with us in being pioneers in introducing a new quality crystal to the marketplace.

THANK YOU . . .

In closing, on behalf of Belleek management and employees, I would like to take this opportunity to thank all of our collectors, our customers, our retailers, and our distributors for participating with us in nurturing that living entity that we cherish as Belleek Pottery. My passion for Belleek grows daily due to the support from all of you. I particularly wish to thank Lady Langham for giving us the opportunity and the forum to address Belleek Today.

GEORGE G. MOORE

Belleek Marks

The Belleek mark 'Without which none is Genuine'.
An Irish Wolfhound with its head turned back to face a Round Tower (believed to be Devenish Round Tower on Devenish Island in Lower Lough Erne). To the right of the Tower is an Irish harp. Below, two sprigs of shamrock border the ends of the banner carrying the word 'BELLEEK'.

FIRST PERIOD BLACK MARK 1863–1890 [Right]
Early pieces of parian leaving the pottery were either impressed with the word 'BELLEEK' or 'BELLEEK, CO FERMANAGH'. Others were impressed and marked with the Belleek 1st period mark. The colour of the mark during this period was predominantly black but other colours were sometimes used, amongst them red, blue, orange, green and brown. Some pieces of Belleek also carry the British Patent Office registration mark, which gives the date of registration, not the date of manufacture.

SECOND BLACK MARK 1891–1926 [Above]
Belleek changed its mark to comply with the McKinley Tariff Act of 1891, requiring imports to the USA to specify the country of origin. A second banner was added below the first mark, carrying the words 'CO FERMANAGH, IRELAND'.

THIRD BLACK MARK 1926–1946 [Above]
A stamp with the Gaelic words 'DEANTA IN EIRINN' (Made in Ireland) and the registered trademark number 0857 was added below the banner.

FIRST GREEN or FOURTH MARK 1946–1955
The mark remained the same but had a colour change.

SECOND GREEN or FIFTH MARK 1955–1965
To identify that the Belleek mark was registered in the USA the letter R within a circle was added above the banner carrying the words 'CO FERMANAGH, IRELAND'.

THIRD GREEN or SIXTH MARK 1965–1981
The mark was reduced in size and the words 'CO FERMANAGH' deleted, leaving 'IRELAND' within a shortened banner.

FIRST GOLD or SEVENTH MARK 1980
The same as the Third Green, but another colour change to Gold.

THORN PLATE *(DS.22)*, DOUBLE BOY SHELL *(VS.20) see page 23*.

INTRODUCTION

THE story of Belleek and how the Pottery came into being is remarkably interesting and one which would merit a detailed study on its own. However, this is not a book on the history of Belleek or the Pottery but rather a pictorial tribute to the porcelain produced there. Nonetheless, no book on Belleek would be complete without some mention of the past.

Belleek is strategically situated on the river Erne, two and a half miles downstream from Lough Erne. In the past, the fast-flowing river tumbled over rapids and waterfalls in its rush to reach the Atlantic Ocean. At Belleek the river hurled itself over one such fall, at the foot of which was a calm pool with a large flat rock, known in Gaelic as *Beal Leice*, which literally translates as 'the ford mouth of the flagstone'.

Hundreds of years before any settlement, the flagstone was well known as a crossing place and Belleek's strategic significance is illustrated by the fact that the Vikings used to camp by the ford and later the Normans built two castles there (both of which were immediately destroyed by the natives). Throughout the early days of Irish history, Belleek is mentioned again and again.

In 1610 Thomas Blennerhassett and his brother, Sir Edward, of Norfolk, England, planters installed by the British, were granted two estates in Fermanagh and founded the town of Belleek. Francis Blennerhassett, son of Sir Edward, built a castle in the area, naming it Hassett's Fort. The family remained in Belleek until 1662 when the estate was sold to the Caldwell family.

Sir James Caldwell, the new owner, gave the castle its present name, Castle Caldwell, and through his line it succeeded to John Caldwell who, returning from military service in America and finding the estate and castle in virtual ruin, assiduously rebuilt it. In 1830 the estate was inherited by his eldest daughter, who had married Major John Colpoys Bloomfield. It was their son, John Caldwell Bloomfield, born in 1823, who was the principal founder of the Pottery.

In fact, the Belleek Pottery owes its origin to *three* men, John Caldwell Bloomfield being the first. The other two, with diverse backgrounds and interests, were Robert Williams Armstrong and David McBirney.

Armstrong, born in 1824, was an architect and civil engineer from County Longford who had settled in Dublin. He went to work in England and by the mid-1850s had built up a substantial practice working as architect to the potteries in the Midlands. He met Bloomfield whilst working for the Worcester Porcelain Company, under the management of Kerr.

McBirney, born in 1804, was a merchant of Dalkey, County Dublin, and a highly successful businessman. He was a director of several railway companies and had other business interests including clothiers of Aston Quay and an Irish woollen warehouse.

Bloomfield was an enterprising landlord and always on the look-out for ways of helping the natives of Belleek to gain employment. Finding rich deposits of fine kaolin and felspar on his land, he became possessed with the idea of founding a porcelain factory which would provide local employment and enhance Ireland's prestige. At the 1853 Dublin International Exhibition, the Worcester Porcelain Co won the highest award for its exhibition of a dinner service called 'Midsummer Night's Dream', produced from Belleek clay. However, in spite of its fine raw material, Ireland had nothing on show and it became even more important for Bloomfield to find the means of getting a pottery established.

Shortly after the 1853 Dublin Exhibition, Bloomfield and Armstrong met. With so much in common, they soon agreed to work together to build the pottery. Bloomfield would provide the land at a nominal rent whilst Armstrong would design, build and manage it. A financial backer was all that was needed and Bloomfield felt he knew the right man – David McBirney. Bloomfield and Armstrong's enthusiasm was such that McBirney was intrigued and travelled to the Worcester Porcelain Factory and then to Belleek. Soon afterwards he agreed to finance the venture. The Pottery would be known as 'D. McBirney & Co'.

Rose Isle was the site chosen. The first notable non-military building constructed in Belleek, 'a fine residence for the Dowager Lady Caldwell', had been on this island, and it was there that the Pottery's foundation stone was laid in July 1857. By the end of the year earthenware was in production, though the factory was not completed till June 1860. Costing some £40,000, Armstrong's design of the Pottery reflected his architectural skill and his understanding of pottery production. It was built to resemble a large country house with a facade of local cut stone and large, well-lit rooms. Figures vary but it seems that the Pottery was built to accommodate up to 500 employees. In fact no more than 250 have ever been employed there.

The site had many advantages. The island was on a bend of the river where the water could be harnessed to give up to 15,000 horsepower, more than adequate to drive the water-wheel required for the Pottery. There were many unemployed people and a wealth of local resources – kaolin, felspar and other raw materials. Ballyshannon, a port three miles downstream, played an important role. Machinery for the pottery was landed at the Salt Works Quay and transported by horse and cart to the Pottery. Most probably the coal required for the Pottery came by the same route until the railway reached Belleek in 1886, having taken nine years' effort and expense by McBirney and Bloomfield to get the line from Enniskillen extended to Ballyshannon via Belleek.

It has also been claimed that water transport on the Erne to Enniskillen and by the Ulster canal to Lough Neagh, Belfast and Derry was a significant asset, but this seems unlikely. The Ulster canal was constructed to narrower dimensions than other canals in Ireland, and goods transported on the canal had to be transferred to special narrow boats. Furthermore the canal was troubled by lack of water, often drying out completely during the summer months.

To begin with, production at the Pottery was confined to earthenware and a wide range of articles were made – high-quality domestic ware, floor tiles, hospital sanitation ware and telephone insulators. Such was the range that on occasions pieces of earthenware turn up whose use is difficult to establish. Being cheaper to produce, earthenware was Belleek's most profitable line and many times was the lifeline upon which the future of the Pottery was to depend. However it was Bloom-field, Armstrong and McBirney's ambition to produce por-celain, as they felt that it was only through porcelain that the Pottery could achieve international recognition, and so in the early days the profit made from the sale of earthenware was ploughed into experiments on parian. The early attempts failed and it was not until late 1863, following the recruitment of William Bromley (foreman), William Gallimore (chief modeller) and other skilled men from Goss, that Belleek parian developed to a quality fit to be marketed.

Bromley and Gallimore were exceptionally qualified and experienced, and it is probable that they brought moulds with them as several Belleek parian pieces are very like those from Goss. Eventually, with the exception of William Henshall, most of these recruits left the pottery, either to return to Goss, as in the case of Bromley and Gallimore, or to go to the USA. However, their knowledge and skills had been passed on to the local people who seemed to have a natural talent for this fine work.

Even then the experiments were continued. Armstrong, always the perfectionist, would not allow products to be marketed unless they met with his approval. It is said barrel-loads of rejects were tipped into the Erne river.

At the 1872 Dublin Exposition the Belleek Pottery had the largest display area in the Irish and English industrial section, showing domestic tableware as well as nine parian statues and the double-spouted chinese tea urn. Gold medals were gained in both categories and Belleek's future looked safe at last. It became fashionable and received commissions from Queen Victoria, the Prince of Wales and members of the nobility. Belleek's order books were full with exports to the United States, Australia and India, and it was also selling well at home. At the Melbourne International Exposition in 1880, the Pottery won yet another Gold medal.

Then in 1882 tragedy struck. McBirney, now 78, caught a cold whilst visiting Cork and died. He had lost fortunes on the Belleek Pottery and a proposed railway system from Belleek to Sligo which never materialised. His son and heir, Robert, who was living abroad, had no interest in the Pottery and wanted it sold. Armstrong of course resisted, claiming a 'gentleman's agreement' forming a partnership between himself and McBir-ney. However, nothing was on paper and Robert refused to recognise his claim. Armstrong had put his entire savings in the Pottery and was now faced with ruin. A fierce legal battle ensued, but this was cut short in 1884 by the untimely death of Armstrong. He was only 59.

As far as the Belleek Pottery was concerned, Armstrong and McBirney had achieved their aim. Belleek porcelain had achieved acclaim for Ireland and Irish porcelain was known throughout the world.

The Pottery closed for a short period as a mark of respect for Armstrong. Then it was put up for sale by public auction, where a group of investors bought it for a song. The price paid was £4,500 for a 999-year lease from 1858, with £50 yearly rent. For this sum the investors purchased the Pottery, the entire stock, the water and fishing rights. Mrs Armstrong was paid a paltry sum for patents she could claim were her's or her husband's.

In September 1884 the Pottery re-opened with a new name – Belleek Pottery Works. Joshua Poole came from Staffordshire to manage the works. The directors were only interested in the Pottery's profitability and were not prepared to continue backing endless experiments on parian, so the production of earthenware was increased at the expense of parian. By the end of the first year the Pottery had succeeded in making a profit – but at a price. Joshua Poole lasted only a few months and left, forced out by the workers who wanted an Irishman and a Catholic. Many of the highly trained and skilled workers found their artistic temperaments clashed with the new regime and also left.

Joshua Poole was succeeded by James Cleary who remained until 1900. Trained by William Gallimore, he was responsible for modelling the Cleary pieces, and during his tenure the Pottery won a Gold Medal at the 1887 Adelaide exhibition in Australia. In 1900 James's brother Edward, having trained and worked in the painting department, took over the management and in the same year another Gold Medal was won, this time at the Paris Exhibition, for the International Centrepiece modelled by Frederick Slater and taking six weeks to create.

The early 80's also saw the start of a long-running dispute with the Erne Drainage Board. In an attempt to control the water levels of Lough Erne and drain the land around the lake shore, they blasted away the waterfalls at Belleek and built sluice gates in lieu. Before doing so they undertook to keep the Erne at a level suitable to drive the Pottery's all-important water-wheel, but the factory had constant water problems thereafter and eventually the Directors took the dispute to court and won.

However, it was too late. These problems, the consequences of the war, and empty order books all had their effect and the workforce dwindled from 180 to 46. In September 1919 the Pottery was up for sale again and a year later, Bernard O'Rourke, a wealthy mill owner from Dundalk, offered the Directors £10,000 for the Pottery. They accepted on the one condition that the property had to continue as a pottery and should not be converted for any other use.

Now called the Belleek Pottery Limited and with new Directors, new life was injected into the Pottery. A succession of managers were appointed and, though most did not stay for very long, one or two had a significant effect on the development of the Pottery. Derrigan came from Stoke-on-Trent but only stayed for two years. He was succeeded by K. E. Loed from Hungary who modernised the works and put much effort into reviving trade abroad, particularly in the United States. He introduced a number of new ranges and also engaged the services of Madame Boroniuxz, a fellow Hungarian. Madame Boroniuxz introduced the Celtic range, taking inspiration from the Books of Kells. K. E. Loed's ideas were good but the old markets no longer existed and it proved difficult to find new outlets so soon after the war. In 1925 J. F. Dolan took over the management until his death in 1931. He was followed by Michael Dolan who managed the Pottery for a year before a Mr Upton came out from England and held the job for two years. He made cuts to the parian and concentrated on earthenware, so much so that he became known as 'the earthenware man'. Mr Upton also added the words 'Melvin Ware' to the trademark for earthenware. During this period Belleek sold its water rights to the Erne Drainage Board and the dispute with them was finally settled. Also, in 1930, a fire destroyed the Company's records and most of the history of the firm was lost.

Then in 1934 Harry Arnold took over as manager and the Pottery at last entered a stable and continuous period of management. Harry managed for seven years before handing over to his brother Eric Arnold in 1940. Eric kept the position for 26 years. It was his tenure which saw the Pottery through World War II. This period was very hard and once more the management turned to earthenware for survival. Earthenware required less china clay and lower firing temperatures and was therefore easier and more economic to produce, especially as the raw materials were hard to obtain and coal was rationed. Production had to be reduced and exports became almost non-existent. Despite these difficulties, with some ingenuity, small amounts of parian and especially baskets continued to be produced. Hot spots in the kilns were used for these pieces during the firing of earthenware. At the end of the war Eric acquired two new kilns and, once installed, the very high and even temperatures required for the firing of parian at last became possible. Production of earthenware ceased.

After many years of struggle the Pottery seemed to have found its way again. Now the Pottery could hardly keep up with the demand, with the order book full for both domestic and overseas markets. In 1952, after nearly one hundred years of coal burning, during which time the Pottery must have consumed thousands of tons of coal, electric kilns were installed. The Pottery had full employment with a complement of 240 workers – the largest number ever employed there.

However, by 1982 the Pottery was fighting for survival again. This time the Northern Ireland Industrial Development Board rescued it. Roger Troughton was appointed Managing Director and the work force, which in 1981 totalled 250, was reduced to around 120. With these and other efficiencies the Pottery was once again on a firm footing and put up for sale again. Roger Troughton headed a consortium which successfully bought it and with his influence the Collectors Society was formed and gathered momentum. In 1982 the first official Collectors' Tour took place and Commander Fred Gary became the first recipient of the coveted 'Hall of Fame' award.

Then, in 1988, Powerscreen International, an engineering company, purchased the pottery from Troughton. Barry Cosgrove was installed as the Managing Director and a major improvement programme was carried out with the International Fund for Ireland. Now the Belleek Pottery, with a new Visitors' Centre, a restaurant, museum and an audio-visual theatre, attracts over 70,000 visitors a year.

Finally, in March 1990, George Moore, originally from Dundalk, now settled in California, purchased the pottery from Powerscreen.

CHAPTER I

Parian

PARIAN is the name given to the white biscuit porcelain primarily associated with figure modelling. The name derives from its close similarity to the white marble mined on the island of Paros in the Aegean Sea. These figures were very popular, being well modelled and having great sculptural appeal, but costing much less than marble.

The development of bisque figures seems to have originated in Europe in the 18th Century. Derby, and then Minton, were the main English potteries noted for its production up to 1840, but by 1851 Copeland had taken the lead and claimed to be the inventors of parian.

Even now the making of parian figures is a highly skilled craft, so in the early days of its development it would have been still more difficult, particularly in regard to temperature control in the coal-fired ovens. Figures are cast in moulds from slip, several moulds being required for each figure. The casts are assembled into a copy of the original model, and all the parts which are liable to warp or move during firing are carefully supported by props. These props have to be coated with powder to prevent adhesion and are made of the same material as the figure so as to be subject to similar contraction in the kiln. The model is then left to stand for two or three days to ensure it is dry enough not to crack during firing in the biscuit oven.

Baking commences, taking sixty to seventy hours at a high temperature. The fires are then drawn and the oven gradually cooled. When the statue is cold, the props are removed and any flaws dealt with. It is embedded in sand-filled saggers which support the statue as it is re-fired for vitrification. During manufacture parian statues contract by about 15%: 3% through evaporation before firing and a further 12% during the first firing.

In the *Art Journal* of 1870, Belleek parian was highly praised for its quality and marble-like appearance. Belleek's first major triumph was at the Dublin Exhibition of 1872. It was by far the largest display and included nine Figurines and Busts, the Prince of Wales Ice Pail, Comports, Centre Pieces, and the Chinese Tea Urn with the double-spouted kettle on a dragon stand.

ERIN (*ST. 10*) [Opposite]
Initially called 'Hibernia Awaking from her Slumbers', Erin is the most significant statue to be produced by Belleek as she symbolises the dawning of the Pottery. The Spirit of Ireland stands in her strap sandals on the Belleek 'flagstone', with the waves of Lough Erne washing them, and her robe flowing over an Irish harp behind her and a Celtic cross to her left. She is unveiling an urn inscribed with the words 'Belleek Pottery' and representing the first ceramic piece to be produced by the Pottery. It has been suggested that W. Boyton Kirk modelled this statue. Rare.

FOUR FERMANAGH VASES [Top right]
(From R–L) The largest vase is the green stage, just out of the mould. The next one is in the biscuit stage. The 'blue' shade vase is the same biscuit stage with glaze applied ready for the final firing and the last one is the finished product.

PARIAN FIRING FLAW [Right]
This close-up of Crouching Venus shows clearly how this piece must have been over-supported during firing, causing her foot to lift off the base.

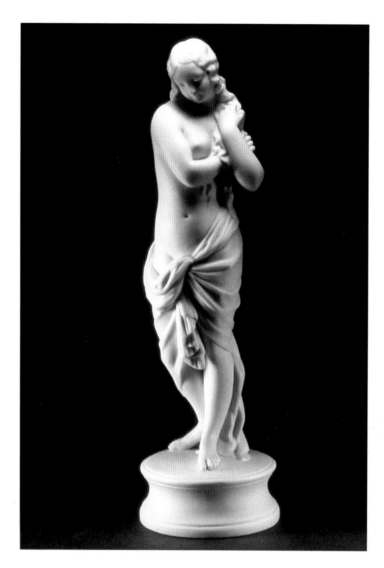

FIGURE OF BATHER *(ST.2)* [Above]
A very rare piece. *From Del Domke's collection.*

LESBIA *(ST.21)* [Top right]
Lesbia crying into one of her hands whilst holding the dead sparrow in the other. *From Del Domke's collection.*

LESBIA, WITH BIRD ON HER SHOULDER *(ST.20)* [Right]
A Roman beauty whose real name was Clodia. The myth tells us that she had a pet sparrow (shown on her shoulder) which she loved so much that one day she crushed it to death, whilst holding it in her hands. *From Del Domke's collection.*

PRISONER OF LOVE *(ST. 26)* [Left]
Giovanni Fontana (1818–1874; born in Carrara; lived and worked in London, exhibiting at the RA between 1852 and 1868) is reputed to have had the original idea for this romantic piece. A maiden, held captive by a chain of flowers and with a pair of doves at her feet. 26″ × 11.73″ wide. Rare. *From Del Domke's collection.*

BUST OF CLYTIE *(ST. 8)* [Above]
In Greek classical mythology Clytie was a water nymph who fell passionately in love with Apollo, God of the Sun. Apollo would rise in the east each morning and drive his fiery chariot across the sky westwards until in the evening he would disappear. Clytie would spend her days watching Apollo cross the sky but her love was unrequited; eventually the Gods took pity on her and turned her into a sunflower – hence the mythological explanation for sunflower heads which turn with the sun.

CROUCHING VENUS *(ST. 9)* [Left]
Venus was originally the Roman Goddess of Growth and the Beauty of Orderly Nature; subsequently, Venus became identified with Aphrodite, Goddess of Love. The Belleek statue was taken from a plaster cast found in Castle Caldwell and identified in 1934 by Brigadier Price (Mr Armstrong's grandson) as being a copy of a fourth century BC Greek sculpture in the Louvre. *From Mrs McElroy's collection.*

HORSE BEING CRUSHED BY A SNAKE (ST.15)

The horse is after the French bronze of Napoleon's horse, Marengo. The subject reflects the struggle of nature. Belleek introduced the piece in the 1880s, and re-introduced it in 1973–4, when a few pieces were made. The piece was also made in parian by William Adams & Co in 1860.

SHAKESPEARE (ST.30)

THE CAVALIER (ST.4)

Bearded, belted and spurred, complete with hat, cloak, gauntlets and pistol. Clearly depicts the Royalist costume during the reign of Charles I. The Cavalier's companion is the Roundhead, showing the Puritan costume during the same period. A very rare figure which was only in production for a short time. *From Berdell Dickinson's collection.*

BUST OF CHARLES DICKENS *(ST.5)*
Charles John Huffamm Dickens (1804–1870), the renowned author.
Some Charles Dickens busts have W.W.C. Gallimore's name
impressed on the back. 14". This bust is very similar to one made by
the Goss potteries. *Photograph reproduced by kind permission of the Trustees
of the Ulster Museum.*

AFFECTION *(ST.1)* [Above right]
From Del Domke's collection.

VENUS AND SHELL *(ST.32)* [Right]
From Frances Horton's collection.

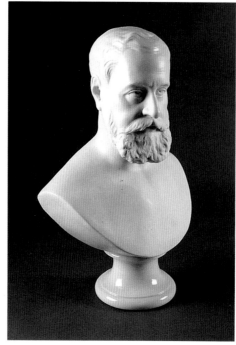

BUST OF QUEEN OF THE HOPS *(ST.27)* [Above left]
From Del Domke's collection.

BUST OF LORD JAMES BUTLER *(ST.18)* [Above centre]
It has not been possible to establish why Belleek made a bust of Lord
Butler. Lady Butler who was an artist, is said to have been the
modeller. *Photograph courtesy The National Museum of Ireland.*

GIRL BASKET FLOWER CARRIER *(ST.11)* [Above right]
The figures vary, some girls carry baskets of flowers, others carry
grapes. *Photograph courtesy The National Museum of Ireland.*

BUST OF SORROW *(ST.31)* [Above]
From Fred and Betty Gary's collection.

BUST OF JOY *(ST.19)* [Left]
From Fred and Betty Gary's collection.

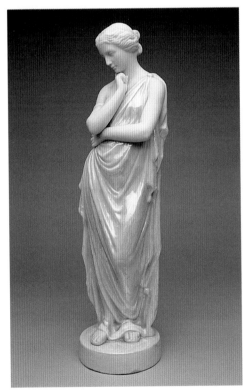

BUST OF WESLEY *(ST. 33)* [Top]
Beside the mould used for this particular piece. Notice how much larger the mould is in comparison to the finished figure. *From the Belleek Potteries collection.*

MEDITATION *(ST. 25)* [Above]
A popular figure: her robes are glazed and sometimes coloured a light pink. She was made during most periods. *From Del Domke's collection.*

GROUP OF FOUR GREYHOUNDS, CHAINED *(ST. 13)* [Above]
The two sitting greyhounds are from the same moulds as the single male and female greyhounds. Note the dogs are chained with ceramic chains. Modelled by the Reverend Halahan Dunbar. *Photograph reproduced with kind permission of the Trustees of the Ulster Museum.*

CHAPTER II

Centre Pieces

Kept at Belleek is a unique photograph album dated around 1872. The first 141 photographs have captions written beside them which are thought to have been entered by Mr Armstrong himself. More photographs have been added at a later date, of which some are entitled 'Paris Exhibition Samples'. All of the important Centre Pieces made by Belleek feature in this Album.

The Belleek range of Centre Pieces is comparatively small, and some make up a part of Dessert Services. Also some of the pieces under this heading could arguably have been entered under Vases, as flowers could be arranged in them, but on balance they are too large and decorative to be used sensibly as vases.

By far the largest and most spectacular is the International Centre Piece especially made for the Paris Exhibition of 1900 where it won a Gold Medal. Intricately made with a delicate pierced throat, the vase symbolised Ireland, featuring not only the harp but also the wolfhounds. There is a fine example of this piece in the front entrance of the Pottery.

INTERNATIONAL CENTRE PIECE *(CP. 7)* [Opposite]
One of the Pottery's most elaborate pieces. Designed by Frederick Slater and reputed to have taken seven weeks to create, it is probable that the flowers are the work of William Henshall. The piece won the Gold Medal for the Pottery at the Paris Exhibition in 1900. 28″ high and 16″ wide. The centre piece illustrated was bought by Miss Florence Birks for the Birks Museum, Dectur, Illinois, from the Horace Manning Mann collection in 1987. The Museum was created in 1981 in recognition of Florence and Jenna Birks who provided all the Belleek and most of the other wonderful pieces of porcelain in the Museum.

PRINCE OF WALES CENTRE PIECE *(CP. 11)* [Above left]
The top is not original, being a Tridacna bread plate, but illustrates the sort of 'marriage' sometimes found.

MINSTREL CENTRE PIECE *(CP. 10)* [Above right]
The putti playing musical instruments are the same as the Minstrel Paperweights. This piece was acquired by the Museum in 1883. 1st period. *Courtesy The National Museum of Ireland.*

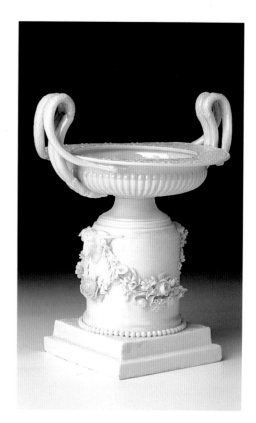

HIPPIRITUS CENTRE PIECE *(CP. 5)* [Top left]
The shells sit on a marine base with smaller shells, starfish and snails.
The moulds of these large shells were also used in other pieces. 11″
highest point.

TRIPLE TULIP CENTRE PIECE *(CP. 20)* [Top centre]
A beautiful example of this popular piece. 12″ high. *From Dr & Mrs
Steinberg's collection.*

TAZZA ON FLOWERED PEDESTAL *(CP. 19)* [Top right]
Very unusual to find complete. 1st period only. 8.5″ high. *From
Maureen and Graham Munton's collection.*

IMPERIAL CENTRE PIECE *(CP. 6)* [Above left]

AMPHORA [Above]
All three sizes. The Amphorae have several finishes: plain white
gilded, and painted.

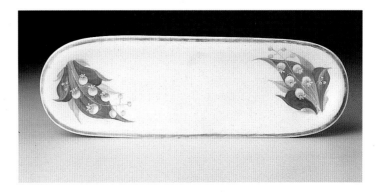

COMPORT PIERCED AND LIDDED *(CP.4)* [Top left]
A very unusual piece, jewelled and pierced, much in the style of Royal
Worcester. Cutting the holes in this piece would not only have taken a
considerable amount of time but the piece required to be kept damp
whilst the cutting was taking place otherwise it would become too
brittle, and the cutting would not work. *From Dr and Mrs Steinberg's
collection.*

WATER LILY ON ROCKS *(CP.22)* [Above left]
*Photograph reproduced by kind permission of the Trustees of the Ulster
Museum.*

PRINCE OF WALES CENTRE PIECE *(CP.11)* [Top right]
Another view of a Prince of Wales centre piece. The horse also figures
on the lid of the Ice Pail. The plate on the top of this piece is the
correct one. 13″ High. Very rare in perfect condition. *From Charles and
Andy Oster's collection.*

BELLEEK MARKS [Centre right]
The Comport (top) with that of a toothbrush dish, both having the
same unusual colour.

THE TOOTHBRUSH DISH [Above right]
This piece is in fact porcelain, not earthenware as might be expected.

CHAPTER III
Vases, Spills and Cornucopias

THE dictionary tells us that a vase 'is an ornamental container to hold flowers and water', but this is clearly an over-simplified definition. For instance the Spill Vase was designed to be placed on the mantel shelf to hold spills used to take a light from the fire before the days of matches.

In fact it has been quite difficult to decide what in the Belleek range constitutes a vase as opposed to an ornament and it seems that Belleek has had this problem too. When registering the Echinus Footed Bowl and the Prince of Wales Ice Pail they were described as 'Vases'. However in the pottery photograph album the Echinus Footed Bowl is described as a sugar bowl and the Ice Pail as an Ice Pail. Among other Vases registered by Belleek were the Cleary Spill Pot, the Marine Vase, the Water Lily Vase and the Flying Fish Vase.

Many of Belleek's vases depict nature, particularly the sea, with shells and dolphins in great abundance. Mrs Armstrong is credited with this influence as she was a well-known landscape painter and had exhibited in the Royal Hibernian Academy before her marriage in 1848. Other designs like the Nautilus on Coral or the Hand Holding Basket are to be found made by other potteries like Royal Worcester and Goss.

ROSE ISLE VASES *(VS.202)* [Above left]
Named after the Island on which the pottery is built. Illustrated front and back decoration of a pair. 2nd period. *From Beatrice McElroy's collection.*

PRINCE ARTHUR VASES *(VS.2)* [Left]
Named after Prince Arthur William Patrick Albert (1850–1942), third son of Queen Victoria. This vase is available flowered or unflowered. *(VS.3)* 3rd period.

PRINCE ARTHUR VASE *(VS.2)* [Above]
Back and front of this unusual vase. 3rd period. *From Fred and Betty Gary's collection.*

COVERED VASE *(VS.63)* [Opposite]
Reproduced by kind permission of the Trustees of the Ulster Museum.

17

[Top left]

TRIPLE FISH VASE *(VS.98)*
DOUBLE FISH VASE *(VS.97)*

All 1st period. These vases are difficult to find undamaged. The fish often have damage to their mouths and the butterflies are frequently restored, which is hard to detect. Available coloured or plain.

DOUBLE FISH WITH NAUTILUS SHELL *(VS.100)* [Top right]
An unusual fish vase, showing Belleek's ingenuity in uniting different pieces to add to their range. 2nd period. *From Betty and Don Clinton's collection.*

BIRD TREE STUMP VASE *(VS.12)* [Above]
On earlier examples the range of flowers and abundance of applied work is quite wonderful. Unfortunately the birds are often damaged. Made in all periods. 2nd period.

TWO BIRD TREE STUMP VASES *(VS.12)* [Above]
The size of the later vase is smaller, and the quantity and quality of flowers has deteriorated. 2nd period and gold mark. *From Fred and Betty Gary's collection.*

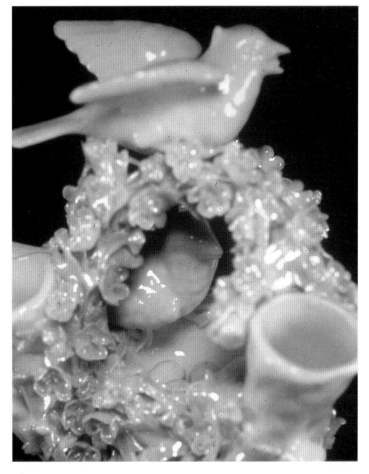

BIRD TREE STUMP VASE *(VS. 12)* [Above]
A very special version of this vase with the bird sitting on the edge of her nest, showing the eggs beneath her. *From Del Domke's collection.*

BIRD TREE STUMP VASE *(VS. 12)* [Top right]
Close-up of the above showing clearly the eggs on which the bird is sitting.

NILE VASES *(VS. 168)* [Right]
On some of the earlier vases the leaves are coloured light pink or green. Made during most periods.

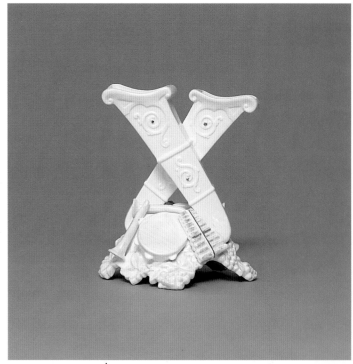

TRIPLE TULIP VASE *(VS.238)* [Above]
2nd period. *From Del Domke's collection.*

QUIVER VASE *(VS.180)* [Top right]
1st period.

[Centre right]
Left to right
TULIP VASE SINGLE *(VS.235)*
A rare vase. 2nd period.
HAREBELL VASE *(VS.124)*
A popular shape used throughout all periods. 2nd period.
PANEL VASE *(VS.175)*
Small. A popular shape. Available in two sizes, plain, coloured or
decorated with shamrocks. 2nd period.

[Right]
Left to right
TRIPLE FLOWER HOLDER *(VS.104)*
TRIPLE HIPPIRITUS VASE *(VS.129)*
Easily distinguished from the Hippiritus centre piece, which has a
large flute in the centre.

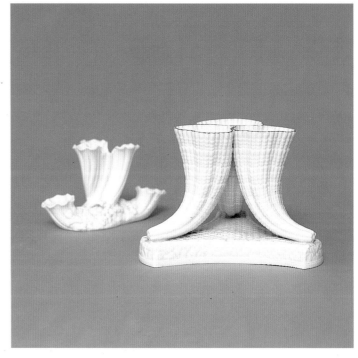

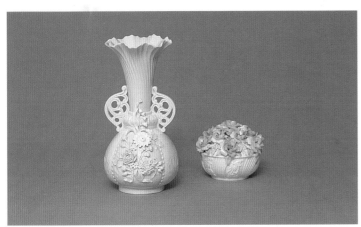

MOON SHELL WITH TRUMPET VASE *(VS. 162)* [Top left]
Two 'moon-shaped' shells (also used in Dolphin Shell Vase) with a
centre trumpet. Tinted in pink or green. A very unusual piece. 2nd
period. *From Mrs McElroy's collection.*

[Centre left]
Left to right
PRINCESS VASE *(VS. 178)*
2nd period. Available unflowered.
ROSE BOWL *(CP. 15)*

PRINCESS VASE *(VS. 179)* [Left]
Unflowered. 2nd period. Note that the shells, which are usually
covered with the applied flowers, have been picked out in pink. *From
Murray and Eunice Robinson's collection.*

CELERY SPILL *(VS. 45)* [Top right]
Rare. 1st period.
INDIAN CORN SPILL *(VS. 136)*. Good colouring. 1st period.

[Above]
Left to right
IVY TREE STUMP SPILL *(VS. 148)*
Available with coloured ivy. 1st period.
IVY TRUNK STUMP SPILL *(VS. 149)*
A popular shape found in most periods, plain or decorated with
shamrocks. 1st period.
CANE SPILL *(VS. 32)*
Small. The ribbon holding the canes is sometimes coloured. Available
in three sizes. 1st period.
INDIAN CORN SPILLS *(VS. 136)*
A pair of popular shaped spills found in most periods, plain, coloured
green, and cob.

[Above]
BOY WITH FISH SPILL (*VS.22*)
1st period.
FISH SPILL COLOURED (*VS.96*)
An example of Belleek's variety of glazing – the fish itself is not glazed
whilst the fins and base are. 1st period.

[Top right]
Left to right
FISH SPILL (*VS.96*)
Watch for damage on this piece. 1st period.
SEA HORSE FLOWER HOLDER (*VS.206*)
Sometimes the sea horses are coloured chocolate or turquoise, which
makes them very attractive. The mould for this sea horse is the same as
the one used on the Prince of Wales Ice Pail. 1st period.
CONCH SHELL VASE (*VS.57*)
Some are crested. 1st period and impressed.
FLYING FISH (*VS.112*)
Watch for damage. 1st period.
ROCK SPILL (*VS.195*)
Middle size. Available in three sizes.

[Centre right]
TRIPLE ROOT SPILL (*VS.199*)
Rare. 2nd period.
SINGLE ROOT SPILL (*VS.197*)
Rare. 2nd period.

[Above]
Back
CLAM SHELL WITHOUT GRIFFIN (*VS.50*)
This wonderful coloured piece was made with and without the Griffin.
1st period.
Left to right
CARDIUM SHELL ON CORAL (*VS.38*)
Illustrated plain and pink trim. Size 2. Four sizes. Both 1st period.
SEA HORSE FLOWER HOLDER (*VS.206*)
2nd period.

[Top left]

BOY SHELL, DOUBLE (VS.20)

A beautiful example of Belleek's fine work. Only the shell is glazed; the rest is delicately coloured and left matt. The boy is the same as is used on the large Triboy Comport. A rare piece and it is even more unusual to find a pair. 1st period.

TRIDACNA PLATE (TTR.26)

The blue colour on the plate is most unusual. 3rd period.

[Top right]

THORN PLATE (DS.22)

The blue finish on the Thorn plate is unusual. 2nd period.

BOY SHELL, DOUBLE BOY (VS.20)

Shell which is glazed throughout. 1st period.

[Above]

SHELL FLOWER HOLDER (VS.212)

Part of a set of four curved flower holders. 1st period.

SHELL PLATEAUX (MI.115)

1st period. Available in three sizes and a wide variety of decoration.

SHELL BISCUIT BOX (TSH.42)

With lid. Three sizes. 1st period.

SHELL SALT (TSH.51)

Wide variety of decoration. 1st period.

CLAM SHELL WITH GRIFFIN (VS.48) [Above]

Hard to find with the Griffin in good condition. *From Del Domke's collection.*

[Top left]

Left to right

THISTLE VASE *(VS.226)*

Available but often badly damaged. 2nd period.

HONEYSUCKLE VASE *(VS.130)*

Sometimes decorated with shamrocks. 1st period.

VIOLET HOLDER *(VS.257)*

1st period.

HAND HOLDING FAN *(VS.122)*

2nd period. *From Graham and Maureen Munton's collection.*

[Above right]

THISTLE VASE *(VS.226)*

Compare this vase with the other Thistle Vase illustrated. In spite of being the same piece they are very different in detail. *From Roy Holihead's collection.*

SHORT THISTLE VASE *(VS.227)*

Unusual version of the Thistle Vase. 2nd period. *From Charles Easthope's collection.*

[Centre left]

CLEARY SPILL *(VS.53)*

Small. 2nd period.

FLOWERED BOWL *(VS.106)*

An unusual piece. 2nd period.

[Left]

Left to right

CLEARY SPILL *(VS.52)*

CLEARLY SPILL *(VS.53)*

CLEARY MUG *(TM.38)*

These three pieces of Cleary illustrate the difference between the good sharp detail on the vase and that from an over-used mould on the mug. The same mug was used for the Cork exhibition logo.

[Top]
Standing
SHELL PLATE *(TSH.77)*
Painted. 3rd period.
Left to right
HENSHALL SPILL *(VS.127)*
Painted. 3rd period.
SNAKE SPILL *(VS.218)*
The snake was painted pink and has since faded. 1st period.
SPECIMEN HOLDER *(VS.220)*
Small size. The shape was also used by Worcester. Plain or decorated and in two sizes.

[Above]
Back
PANEL VASE *(VS.175)*
Plain or decorated with shamrocks. 2nd period.
Left to right
DOLPHIN SPILL *(VS.77)*
Pair. Dolphins can be coloured. 2nd period.
LILY OF VALLEY VASE *(VS.156)*
A popular shape still in production today. 2nd period.
TRIPLE FLOWER HOLDER *(VS.104)*

[Top right]
Back
ONION SPILL *(VS.171)*
Available in two sizes. 2nd period.
Left to right
FORGET-ME-NOT TRINKET BOX *(MI.19)*
2nd period.
BROOCH *(MI.30)*
2nd period.
MEDALLION OF FAME *(MI.52)*
CLEARY SPILL *(VS.53)*

COLLECTION OF IRISH POTS [Above]
These pots come with different decorations and have been made throughout all periods. There is also a creamer to match the smaller pots.

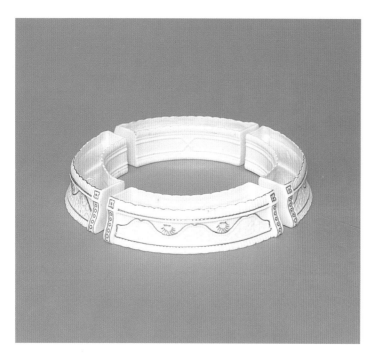

FROG VASE *(VS.115)* [Above]
Large. Available in two sizes. 2nd period.

[Top left]
TRIPLE SHELL SPILL *(VS.214)*
Rare. 2nd period.
NICKEL FLOWER POT *(FP.33)*
Rare. 2nd period.

RING POSY FOR TABLE CENTRE *(VS.190)* [Centre left]
Variation of coloured finishes. Difficult to find a set of all four vases.
1st period.

[Left]
Standing
BASKET DESSERT PLATE *(DS.4)*
Probably a special order with this unusual brown decoration. 1st
period.
Left to right
RAM'S HEAD SPILL *(VS.182)* Rare. 1st period.
CACTUS SPILL *(VS.28)*
An unusual spill, the tulip flower is the same flower as the small tulip
in the large centre piece. 1st period.
VICTORIA SHELL *(VS.255)*
2nd period.
CONE VASE *(VS.58)*
3rd period.

[Top]

ROCK SPILL *(VS.196)*

Small. Available plain or coloured and in three sizes.

NAUTILUS ON CORAL *(VS.164)*

Available coloured or plain.

CORAL AND SHELL VASE *(VS.60)*

Coloured green, pink, or plain.

[Left]

BOXER ON CUSHION *(MI.68)*

SINGLE BOY SHELL *(VS.18)*

It is reputed that Queen Victoria particularly liked the 'Chocolate' finish. Several Belleek pieces have this colour but it was difficult and expensive to produce.

HAND HOLDING BASKET *(VS.121)* [Above]

Rare to find this vase with a Belleek mark. They should not be confused with similar but unmarked pieces produced by other potteries. 1st period. *From Betty and Don Clinton's collection.*

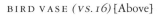

BIRD VASE *(VS.16)* [Above]
Another version of this hand-painted vase with a bird perched on the vase. 2nd period. *From Josephine Corriveau's collection.*

WHELK SHELLS, THREE STANDING *(VS.258)* [Top right]
A previously unrecorded Belleek piece, but it was made by Goss and the mould could have come from there. 2nd period. (The miniature shells on the left are real.) *From Fred and Betty Gary's collection.*

[Centre right]
BOY SHELL SINGLE *(VS.18)*
Another use for the Belleek boy. 1st period.
MARINE VASE *(VS.159)*
It is available in two sizes, coloured or plain. *From Berdell Dickinson's collection.*

[Right]
Left to right
DOLPHIN AND WINKLE *(VS.72)*
.Single. Beautifully coloured piece. 1st period.
SHAMROCK THREE-HANDLED LOVING CUP *(SHA.18)*
Note the quality of painting on the shamrocks. 1st period. Shamrock first period pieces are rare. *From Berdell Dickinson's collection.*

BIRD VASE *(VS. 15)* [Above]
A pair of hand-painted vases, both different. 2nd period. *From Charles Easthope's collection*

[Left]
MASK SUGAR *(TMA. 21)*
Large size. 3rd period.
HENSHALL VASE *(VS. 127)*
2nd period.
ROSE BOWL *(CP. 15)*
Small. 3rd period.
ROSE BOWL *(CP. 14)*
Large. Note the bowl is also mask.

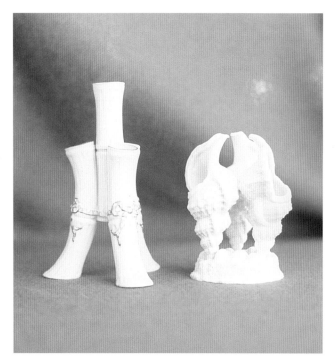

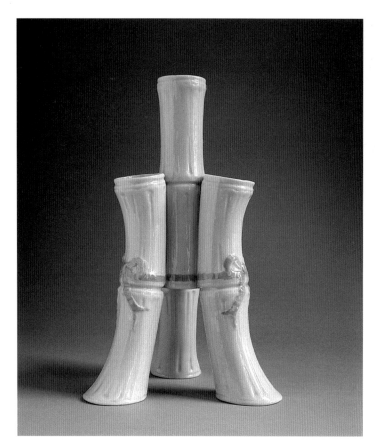

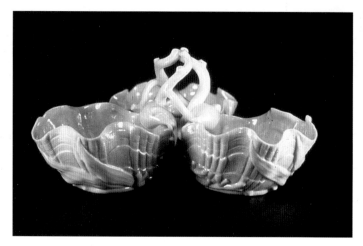

BAMBOO VASE *(VS. 9)* [Above]

[Top left]
Left to right
BAMBOO VASE *(VS. 9)*
Middle size. Gilded ribbon.
WHELK SHELLS *(VS. 258)*
From Fred and Betty Gary's collection

[Top right]
Top back
RATHMORE VASE *(VS. 183)*
Left to right
ELCHO VASE *(VS. 85)*
Probably named after Lord Francis Richard Charteris Elcho (1818–
1914), the future Earl of Wemyss and March, noted for his work in
military reform and ADC to Queen Victoria.
SIX-SIDED SPILL *(VS. 217)*
Fluted and Twisted. To date an unrecorded spill. 2nd period.
FLUTED SPILL *(VS. 111)*
Available in two sizes.
HIPPIRITUS *(VS. 128)*
Single.
HIPPIRITUS *(VS. 128)*
Single. Note the same trumpets, with differing bases.

TRIPLE BUCKET *(VS. 24)* [Above]
An unusual and rare piece. *From Del Domke's collection*

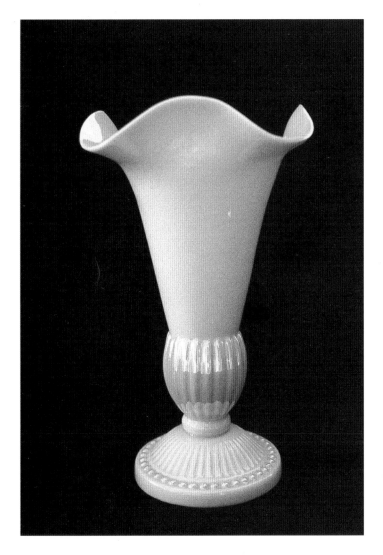

VASE FLUTED (VS.247) [Above]
2nd period. *From Eddie Renshaw's collection.*

[Top right]
DOLPHIN AND SHELL (VS.75)
The pieces which go to make up this vase are used to create other pieces. 2nd period.
LEAF VASE WITH HANDLE (VS.151)
1st period. *From Edith Jacobson's collection.*

(Centre right]
Left to right
FLASK (MI.26)
FLOWER TRUMPET VASE (VS.105)
Triple. An unusual piece – originally from Horace Manning Mann's collection.
ERNE LEAF PLATE (MI.76)
Large. *From Bob McCarthy's collection.*

IRIS VASE (VS.138) [Right]
A very unusual hand-painted vase. 3rd period. *From Liz Stillwell's collection.*

[Above]
Back
BOY WITH FISH SPILL *(VS.22)*
Left to right
ECHINUS FOOTED BOWL *(MI.8)* Missing lid.
SWAN CORNUCOPIA *(VS.223)*
BOY CANDLE HOLDER *(CL.6)*
Pierced. *From Roy Holihead's collection.*

LEINSTER FLOWER HOLDERS *(VS.152)* [Right]
From Josephine Corriveau's collection.

DIANA VASES *(VS.67)* [Above]
Unpierced. *From Eileen O'Neill's collection.*

TRIPLE CARDIUM ON CORAL *(VS.41)* [Right]
Large. Three shells joined by a clump of coral. A delicate and rare
piece, difficult to find perfect. 1st period.

[Above]
Left to right
MARINE JUGS *(JU.59)*
Pair.
VICTORIA BASKET *(VS.254)*

PIERCED SPILLS *(VS.176)* [Left]
From Dr Robert E Gregg's collection.

COMMEMORATIVE VASE *(VS.56)* [Below]
A very interesting vase which bears the faces of Arthur Griffith and
Michael Collins who were both signatories of the treaty signed
between Britain and Ireland in 1921 which led to the Irish Civil War
in 1922. Griffith and Collins both died within 10 days of each other in
August 1922. The sides of the vase have a celtic pattern, highlighted
with gilding. *From Eileen O'Neill's collection.*

CROCODILE SPILL *(VS.64)* [Above]
Reproduced by kind permission of the Trustees of the Ulster Museum.

[Top right]
PIERCED AND LINED VASE *(VS.248)*
Very unusual vase which also comes coloured; there is also a covered
version. 1st period.
SALT GLAZE JUG *(JU.71) From the late Pat Campbell's collection.*

FEATHER VASE *(VS.93)* [Centre right]
Small size. 2nd period. *From the late Pat Campbell's collection.*

MARINE VASE *(VS.160)* [Bottom right]
From the late Pat Campbell's collection.

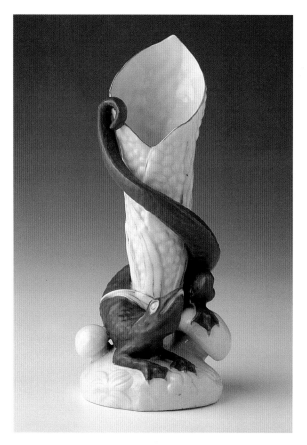

LIZARD VASE *(VS.158)* [Top left]
1st period. *From Margaret and Rodney Capper's collection.*

LILY BASKET *(VS.153)* [Top right]
1st period. *From Margaret and Rodney Capper's collection.*

LILY BASKET *(VS.153)* [Above]
2nd period.

VASE PAINTED FLOWERS AND GILDED *(VS.250)* [Right]
Photograph courtesy The National Museum of Ireland.

SEA HORSE AND SHELL *(VS.205)*
*From the Horace Manning Mann collection. Now part of Margaret and
Rodney Capper's collection.*
SEA HORSE FLOWER HOLDER *(VS.206)* Very rare finishes to these
old favourites. 1st period. *From Margaret and Rodney Capper's collection.*

CHAPTER IV

Miscellaneous Figurines and Ornaments

THE range of miscellaneous items produced by Belleek in its heyday was quite amazing but records are scant and many were probably 'one off' or prototype designs so unrecorded pieces are continually turning up. Unfortunately this lack of information makes it difficult to find out how many of the pieces were made and rarity has to be judged from experience. Among the most unusual pieces are the Carnation, a charming piece, housed in the Dublin Museum and the Turkey, which is well designed and executed in great detail, standing about eight inches high, but difficult to understand why it was made. The Cenotaph is another unusual and interesting piece which seems to have little purpose. It would be reasonable to conclude that these three pieces were 'singles', but the taking into consideration the time and labour involved in preparing the moulds etc for making them, it would seem unlikely that they would have gone to that trouble for 'one offs' pieces unless they were perhaps apprentice pieces or maybe personal gifts etc from craftsmen at the pottery.

Among other designs registered by Belleek, Jack at Sea and Jack on the Shore, were registered on 13 November, 1869 though being re-introduced in the 1st Green period, they remain rare.

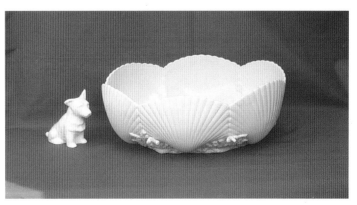

[Top right]
FLOWERED MENU HOLDER *(TM.36)*
FLOWERED BROOCH *(MI.30)*
Note how these brooches are all different. *From Margaret and Rodney Capper's collection.*

[Right]
DOG, SCOTTIE *(MI.42)*
SHELL PLATEAU *(MI.114)*
The dog should give some idea of the very large size of this plateau. *From the late Pat Campbell's collection.*

[Opposite]
ECHINUS FOOTED BOWL *(MI.8)*
1st period. *From Margaret and Rodney Capper's collection.*

BEETLE FLY MATCHBOX *(MI.17)* [Above]
Two views of this rare piece. The lid of the box clearly showing the fly and the underneath of the wings showing the 'match striker'. *From Del Domke's collection.*

[Above]
Left to right
SWANS *(MI.55)*
Large.
SWANS *(MI.56)*
Small with various decorations. Made in most periods.
GREYHOUND *(MI.43)*
Male. Made in pairs, male and female.
PIG *(MI.53)*
Large.
PIG *(MI.54)*
Small. Very popular ornaments. Made during most periods.
Left to right front
BEETLE FLY MATCHBOX *(MI.17)*
The example pictured is missing the lid which forms the wings. Very rare piece. 1st period.
KING CHARLES SPANIEL ON CUSHION PAPERWEIGHT *(MI.66)*
The cushion on this piece is glazed whilst the dog has been left unglazed. 2nd period.
FROG LILY PAD PAPERWEIGHT *(MI.65)*
A later introduction of an earlier piece. Unmarked.

[Centre left]
LEPRECHAUN *(MI.50)*
In Irish folklore a leprechaun is a small, roguish elf. Belleek leprechauns are plain or painted. Occasionally the painting is done later. Most periods.
IRISH POT *(VS.143)*
Medium Irish pot. 3rd black.

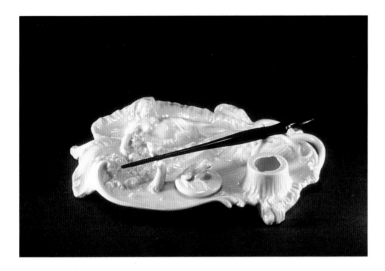

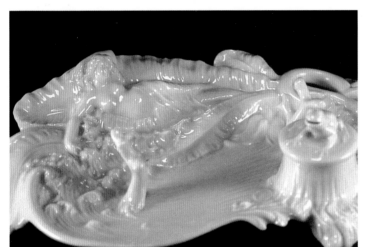

MERMAID INKSTAND *(MI.28)* [Top left]
A mermaid reclines on a shell which forms the pen tray and contemplates a frog sitting on top of the inkwell. *From Del Domke's collection.*

MERMAID INKSTAND *(MI.28)* [Centre left]
A close-up of the mermaid inkstand.

[Bottom left]
Left to right
BELGIAN HAWKER *(MI.38)*
Male.
BOY AND GIRL BASKET CARRIERS *(MI.35 & 36)*
Unpierced.
MINSTREL WITH FLUTE PAPERWEIGHT *(MI.67)*
Putto playing the flute. From a set of four, others being horn, lute, and cymbals players. Rare, and usually found damaged. 1st period.
BELGIAN HAWKER *(MI.37)*
Female. It is possible that Boyton Kirk who worked for the Worcester Porcelain Co. modelled this pair of figures.

[Below right]
BELGIAN HAWKER *(MI.37)*
Female.
BELGIAN HAWKER *(MI.38)*
Male.
A coloured example of this much sought after pair. *From Eileen O'Neill's collection.*

[Bottom right]
THE BELGIAN HAWKERS
From Del Domke's collection.

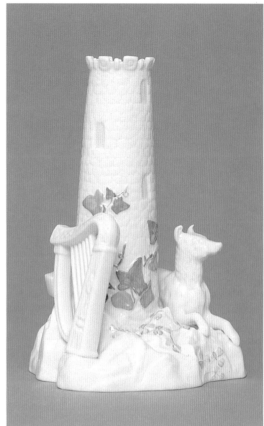

GREYHOUNDS *(MI.43)* [Top left]
Pair of greyhounds, 2nd and 3rd period. Note the base is glazed, but
the dogs remain unglazed.

[Above]
KING CHARLES SPANIEL ON CUSHION PAPERWEIGHT
(MI.66)
Note the intricate gilding on the cushion. 1st period. *From Mrs
William's collection.*
GREYHOUNDS *(MI.43)*
Two dogs. 2nd and 3rd period.
JACK-ON-SHORE TRINKET BOX *(MI.16)*
1st period.

[Top right]
TOWER, HARP AND WOLFHOUND *(MI.59)*
Introduced in 1st green.

[Above right]
TURKEY *(MI.60)*
A surprising piece. Very rare. 2nd period.
FERN FLOWER POT *(FP.23)*
Small size, 2nd period. *From Edith Jacobson's collection.*

[Top left]
Left to right
TRINKET BOX WITH APPLIED SHAMROCKS *(MI.21)*
DIAMOND FLOWER POT *(FP.18)*
CHERUB BOX *(MI.11)*
2nd period.

[Above left]
Left to right
FERN FLOWER POT *(FP.23)*
1st period miniature.
MINSTREL WITH LUTE PAPERWEIGHT *(MI.67)*
CLAM SHELL BOX *(MI.12)*
Covered with coral finial. Very rare. 2nd period. *From Edith Jacobson's collection.*

TOBACCO BREWER *(MI.58)* [Top right]
From Dr and Mrs Steinberg's collection.

JACK-AT-SEA BOX *(MI.15)* [Above right]
HONEYSUCKLE VASE *(VS.130)*
From Dr and Mrs Steinberg's collection.

FLASK *(MI.26)* [Top left]
Very unusual centre decoration. *Photograph reproduced by kind permission of the Trustees of the Ulster Museum.*

FLASK *(MI.26)* [Above left]
There are many stories as to why Belleek made these flasks. One was that the flasks were made to bring back water from the Holy Land. Another story is they were given as retiring presents by the Pottery, but the most probable explanation is that they have a Masonic connection.

PENDANT *(MI.31)* [Top right]
1st period. *From Roy Holihead's collection.*

FLASK *(MI.26)* [Above right]
Decorated and plain.
From Dr and Mrs Steinberg's collection.

[Top]
FORGET-ME-NOT TRINKET BOX *(MI.19)*
Difficult to find these boxes undamaged. 2nd period.

SELECTION OF BROOCHES *(MI.30)*
These show the skills of the Belleek craftsmen. Small well-made flowers in abundance and made to look so natural. All marked 1st period. *From Graham and Maureen Munton's collection.*

FROG LILY PAD PAPERWEIGHT. *(MI.65)* [Above left]
An early example of the frog paperweight. Impressed only 'Belleek County Fermanagh'.

FROG LILY PAD PAPERWEIGHT *(MI.65)* [Above right]
An illustration of the early frog paperweight and the more recent introduction.

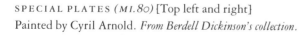

SPECIAL PLATES *(MI.80)* [Top left and right]
Painted by Cyril Arnold. *From Berdell Dickinson's collection.*

BASKET WITH HANDLE FLOWERED *(MI.2)* [Above left]
A unusual pair of baskets; note the handles are two and three loops.

CENOTAPH *(MI.40)* [Centre right] A very unusual piece. 1st period.

INKSTAND APPLE *(MI.27)* [Right]
A rare piece which is difficult to find undamaged. 1st period. *From Don & Betty Clinton's collection.*

PLAQUE WITH ENAMELLED CENTRE *(MI.71)* [Above]
The four panels with scenes depicting game birds and animals are unglazed whilst in the centre there is a small bouquet of hand-painted flowers. The whole is then most intricately gilded. An unusual and interesting plaque. *Photograph reproduced by kind permission of the Trustees of the Ulster Museum.*

EAGLES CRAG PLAQUE *(MI.70)* [Left]
Earthenware, hand-painted and signed Sherrin. *From Mrs McElroy's collection.*

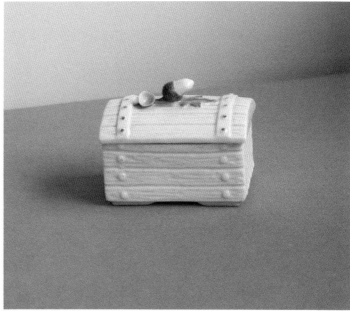

SCENT BOTTLE *(MI.006)* [Above]
A very rare scent bottle. The centre is pierced whilst the scent is held in the wheel around the bottle. *Photograph courtesy The National Museum of Ireland.*

ACORN TRINKET BOX *(MI.10)* [Top right]

CARNATION ON STAND *(MI.34)* [Right]
A life size carnation set on a shell base. *Photograph courtesy The National Museum of Ireland.*

PRINCE OF WALES ICE PAIL *(MI.118)* [Opposite]
Specially made for the Prince of Wales in 1880. The making of this piece is rather special as some of the detail on the pail is so heavy it has to be applied after it comes out of the slip mould. For example, the boy in the front has been applied. The horses on the lid of the Ice Pail have been used in several other pieces made by Belleek. The Mermaids can also be found holding the Echinus pot.

OVAL-FOOTED BASKET *(BS.48)* [Above]
Very unusual basket. The flowers are glazed but the body has been left un-glazed. Large size.

OVAL-FOOTED BASKET *(BS.48)* [Right]
Showing the underside to this basket. *From the late Pat Campbell's collection.*

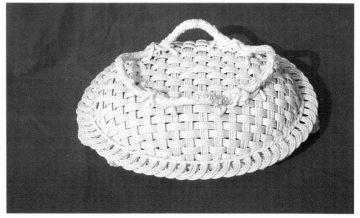

CHAPTER V

Baskets

A mention of the word Belleek conjures up pictures in the mind of the beautiful baskets for which the Pottery is famed – justifiably so for Belleek baskets are second to none. However the skill was first imported from Staffordshire, where a John Smith of Hanley is known to have been making parian baskets as early as 1863, and it was William Henshall, who came from Staffordshire, who introduced basket and flower modelling to Belleek.

The earliest Belleek baskets were flat-rodded and unflowered. Then a small range of round-rodded baskets were introduced which included the Rathmore Basket, the Hawthorn Basket, the Triple Nest Basket and the Henshall Baskets named after William Henshall. With continued popularity the variety was increased.

The manufacture of baskets is understandably complex. The parian ingredients are carefully ground before being mixed with gum arabic in place of the water used to produce the slip for other products. The resultant dough-like mixture is kneaded as though it were bread and then beaten to remove any air. Once ready for use the 'dough' is placed in a 'dod box'. Working like a mincemeat machine, the dod box extrudes the mixture from the box in threads resembling spaghetti. These are cut into lengths and kept 'plastic' until required by covering with a damp cloth.

Modelling is a painstaking process. First the base of the basket is made, woven from two, three or four strands of clay at a time. The base is then placed on a plaster of paris mould and the lattice of side strands laid in place. The basket is finished off with a twisted ribbon of strands and is ready to take the applied flowers. These are all hand-made, using very few tools. Looking carefully at flowers one can quite often notice the fingerprints of the maker.

DATING BASKETS

Baskets are often difficult to date exactly but there are some characteristics which help. Early baskets usually had three or sometimes two strand bases instead of the four strands which were brought in later. Also different impressed or printed pads were normally applied to the base. The table below shows the recognition features for baskets.

When dating baskets, it is important not only to take into account the number of strands and the marks on the pads, but to look carefully at the quality of the flowers and the glaze. The early baskets have a greater variety and abundance of flowers, with a noticeably smooth and rich glaze. Also, apart from a few very delicate coloured baskets, early baskets are white. Lastly, early baskets have handles with thorns which represent briars, whilst later basket handles have grated porcelain applied which is quite different. Baskets without handles should be carefully examined to ensure that the handles have not been removed as a means of disguising damage. It is a very easy matter to overlook.

Date	Strands	Words	Pads	Mark
c. 1865–1889	2/3	Belleek	I	Impressed
	2/3	Belleek Co. Fermanagh	1, 2 or 3	
1890–1920	2/3	Belleek Co. Fermanagh		
		*Ireland	1, 2 or 3	
1921–1954	4	Belleek (R) Co. Fermanagh	I or 2	
		*Ireland		
1955–1979	4	Belleek (R) Co. Fermanagh	I or 2	
1980–1989	4	*Belleek (R) Ireland	I or 2	
1989	4	*Belleek (R) Ireland	Oval Gold	Printed

* The McKinley Act of 1891 required that the country of origin be marked on all imported goods. The capital letter 'R' was added in 1955 as proof of USA registration.

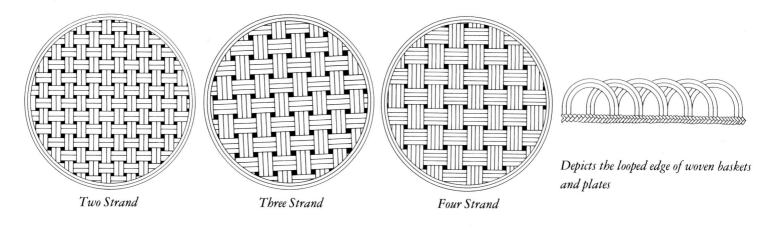

Two Strand   *Three Strand*   *Four Strand*   *Depicts the looped edge of woven baskets and plates*

RATHMORE BASKET

The town of Belleek lies in two 'Townlands'; Rathmore to the east and Finner to the west. The Rathmore Basket is named after the Townland whose ancient origins reach back into early Celtic history, when the *Ulaidh* clan established a fort, *Rath Mohr*, on a hill overlooking Belleek. Now it is the King of baskets.

The Rathmore Basket was one of the earlier introductions. The early baskets have very fine bases, usually three strand, with twisted loops around the top. A ribbon surrounds the whole, which has an abundance of flowers, looped legs, and handles at each end. They were later re-introduced and are in current production.

OVAL COVERED BASKET

If the Rathmore Basket is the King of baskets the Covered Basket must take the place of Queen. It is extremely difficult and costly to make with a high manufacturing failure rate. Apart from the normal hazard of collapsing, if for any reason the lid and the base of the basket should shrink at different rates during firing they no longer fit and both pieces are rejected and destroyed.

RATHMORE BASKET *(BS.54)* [Top left]
Both baskets have restored handles and are three strand, having one pad with Belleek Co. Fermanagh.

RATHMORE BASKET *(BS.54)* [Bottom left]
Note the open three strand base.

OVAL COVERED BASKET, LARGE SIZE *(BS.42)* [Above]
A beautiful example of a large covered basket – but note the missing handles. The handles (grated procelain) on lid give some idea of the date, *c.*1945. 4 strand, Belleek Co. Fermanagh, Ireland.

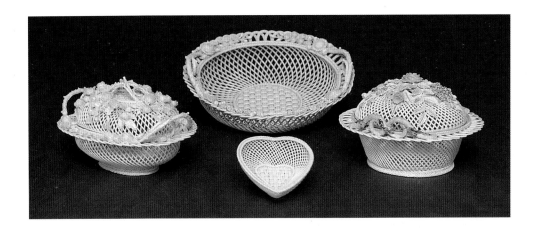

[Top]

OVAL COVERED BASKET, SMALL SIZE (BS.43)
The basket illustrated is exceptionally beautiful with superb glazing. 3 strand, Belleek Co. Fermanagh, Ireland, 1 pad.

OVAL BASKET, LARGE SIZE (BS.44)
3 strand, Belleek Co. Fermanagh, 1 pad.

HEART BASKET (BS.22)
Popular baskets, flowered or unflowered. 4 strand, Belleek Co. Fermanagh, Ireland, 3 pads.

ROUND COVERED FLOWERED BASKET (BS.61)
Belleek R. Ireland, 1 pad

BOAT SHAPE BASKET (BS.4) [Centre left]
Later introduction. Belleek Co. Fermanagh, Ireland, 2 pads.

BOAT ASHTRAY (TM.1) 1st period.

[Bottom left, *Left to right*]

SYDENHAM TWIG SMALL SIZE BASKET (BS.77)
Encrusted with Lily of Valley. 3 strand, Belleek Co. Fermanagh, 1 pad. *From Mrs McElroy's collection.*

SYDENHAM TWIG LARGE SIZE BASKET (BS.75)
Encrusted with roses. 4 strand, Belleek County Fermanagh, 1 pad.

SYDENHAM TWIG MIDDLE SIZE BASKET (BS.76)
3 strand, Belleek Co. Fermanagh Ireland, 1 pad.

SYDENHAM TWIG LARGE SIZE BASKET (BS.75)
2 strand, Belleek Co. Fermanagh, 1 pad.

[Above]

NO. 8 BASKET (BS.41)
A later example of this rare basket. 4 strand. Belleek Co. Fermanagh Ireland R.

CONVOLVULUS BASKET (BS.14)
A later example of a rare basket. 4 strand. Belleek R Ireland
Standing

CAKE PLATE (BS.11)
Round edge, no handles. 4 strand. Belleek R Co. Fermanagh

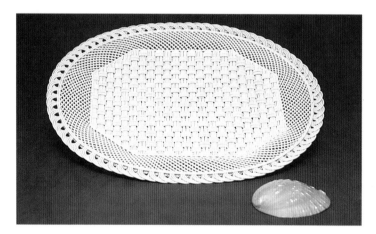

[Above]

SHAMROCK BASKET (BS.71)
Flowered. Both 3 stranded.
OVAL BASKET, SCALLOPED AND ROUND ROD EDGE (BS.50)
3 strand, Belleek Co. Fermanagh Ireland
BIRD'S NEST BASKET (BS.1)
4 strand, Belleek Co. Fermanagh Ireland, 3 pads.
Front
FORGET-ME-NOT BASKET (BS.19)
4 strand. Belleek Co. R Fermanagh.

[Top left] *Standing*
HEXAGON TWIG CAKE PLATE (BS.33)
No handles. 4 strand. Belleek Co. Fermanagh Ireland.
Left to right
HENSHALL'S TWIG (BS.29)
Note the different flowers at each handle. Small size 4 strand.
SHAMROCK BASKET, FLOWERED (BS.71)
3 strand. Belleek Co. Fermanagh.
COLOURED OVAL BASKET (BS.44)
Large. 4 strand. Belleek Co. Fermanagh Ireland.
SHAMROCK BASKET, FLOWERED (BS.71)
3 strand. Belleek Co. Fermanagh.

[Left centre] *Left to right*]
MELVIN BASKET (BS.39)
A late addition to Belleek basket range. 4 strand. Belleek Co. Fermanagh.
HEXAGON TWIG CAKE PLATE (BS.34)
With handles. 4 strand. Belleek R Ireland.
BOSTON BASKET (BS.5)
In spite of being a later addition to Belleek's range it is hard to find. 4 strand, Belleek Co. Fermanagh Ireland.
Centre front
SHAMROCK BASKET, FLOWERED (BS.71)

TRAY WOVEN (BS.80) [Left centre]
Oval. A difficult tray to make. 4 strand. Belleek Co. Fermanagh on 1 pad.

[Left]
OVAL BASKET (BS.44)
Large. 3 strand, Belleek Co. Fermanagh, 1 pad.
HENSHALL'S TWIG BASKET (BS.29)
Beautiful two strand basket. Not many produced. Belleek Co. Fermanagh, 1 pad.
SHAMROCK BASKET (BS.71)

SHAMROCK BASKET *(BS.71)* [Top left]

Flowered. Two shamrock baskets. Note different flowers on each corner; later baskets have the same flower all the way round. Both 3 strand.

SYDENHAM TWIG *(BS.77)* [Above]

Small. A beautiful example of a two strand Sydenham Twig Basket. *From Liz Stillwell's collection.*

OVAL BASKETS [Left]

Large, small, and later coloured version of large basket.

RING STAND MINIATURE *(BS.86)* [Below]

4 strands. *From Del Domke's collection.*

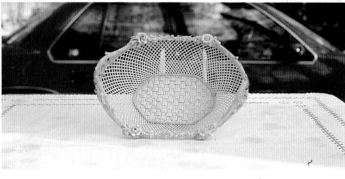

[Above]

Back

RING STAND *(BS.86)*

From Roy Hollihead's collection.

Left to right

TWIG SPECIAL BASKET *(BS.84)*

Small. A beautiful example of a two strand early basket. *From Roy Hollihead's collection.*

HENSHALL'S TWIG *(BS.29)*

Small. 4 strand.

BIRD'S NEST BASKET *(BS.I)*

4 strand. *From Charles Easthope's collection.*

HEART BASKET, FLOWERED *(BS.24)*

4 strand. *From Charles Easthope's collection.*

BOSTON NO LOOPED EDGE *(BS.6)* [Centre left]

4 strand. *From Josephine Corriveau's collection.*

OVAL BASKET WITH FLOWERS AND SCALLOPED EDGE, LARGE *(BS.49)* [Left]

4 strand. *From Josephine Corriveau's collection.*

HENSHALL'S TWIG *(BS.25)* [Below left]
4 strand. *From Margaret Power's collection.*

HENSHALL'S TWIG *(BS.28)* [Below right]
Middle size 4 strand. *From Dr Robert Gregg's collection.*

HENSHALL'S TWIG *(BS.25)* [Bottom]
A beautiful example of an early 2 strand basket. *From the Birks
Museum's collection.*

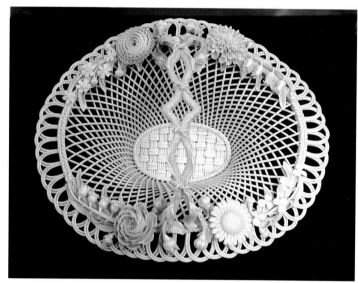

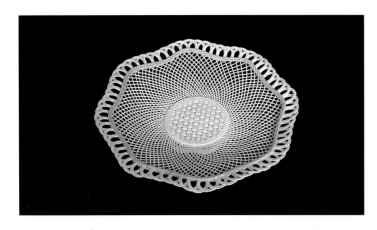

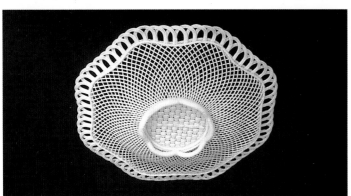

PENTAGONAL PLATE ON FEET *(BS.53)* [Top left]
From Dr Robert Gregg's collection.

PENTAGONAL PLATE *(BS.53)* [Centre left]
Underside of the above.

ROUND BASKET *(BS.64)* [Above right]
Flowered with handle. 4 strand. *From Frances Horton's collection.*

HEXAGON BASKET *(BS.31)* [Bottom left]
4 strand. *From Josephine Corriveau's collection.*

UNITED STATES OF AMERICA BICENTENNIAL PLATE
(BS.85) [Below right]
It is believed that less than eighteen of these were made. *From Margaret Power's collection.*

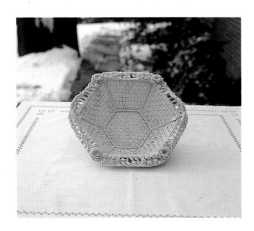

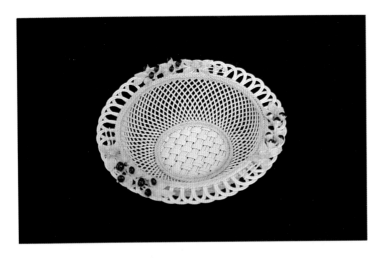

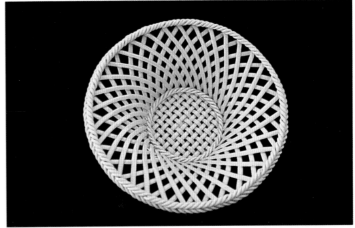

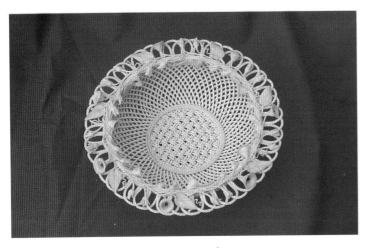

BLACKBERRY BASKET *(BS.3)* [Top left]
4 strand. *From Dr Robert Gregg's collection.*

[Centre left]
ROUND COVERED FLOWERED BASKET *(BS.62)*
ROUND COVERED FLOWERED BASKET *(BS.61)*
From the late Pat Campbell's collection.

CONVOLVULUS BASKET *(BS.14)* [Bottom, left and right]
Two views of this very rare basket. To give extra detail to the basket
the strands were twisted. 2 strand. *From the late Pat Campbell's
collection.*

ITALIAN FLAT TWIG BASKET *(BS.38)* [Top right]
This basket also comes with looped edges. *From Eddie Renshaw's
collection.*

ROUND COVERED FLOWERED BASKET *(BS.61)* [Centre right]
An early example of this basket. 3 strand. *From the late Pat Campbell's
collection.*

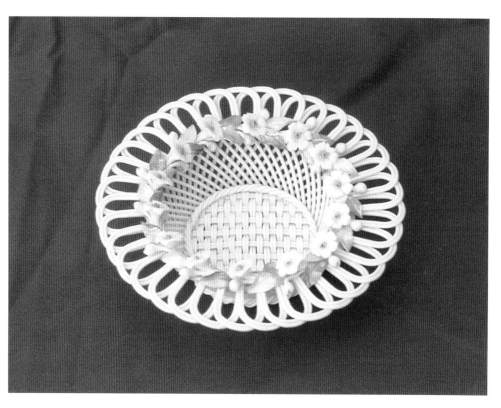

HAWTHORN BASKET *(BS.20)* [Above]
Small size. A most exquisite basket with delicately painted flowers. 2 strand. *From the late Pat Campbell's collection.*

ITALIAN FLAT TWIG BASKET *(BS.38)* [Bottom right]
These baskets were the forerunners to Belleek's well-known round flowered baskets. Rare.

SHAMROCK A C BASKET WITH ROD EDGE *(BS.72)*
From the late Pat Campbell's collection.

HEXAGON A J BASKET *(BS.32)* [Below]
Very rare basket. 3 strand. *From the late Pat Campbell's collection.*

[Below]
ROUND A E BASKET *(BS.63)*
4 strand.

OVAL A O BASKET *(BS.50)*
With round rod edge. 4 strand. *From the late Pat Campbell's collection.*

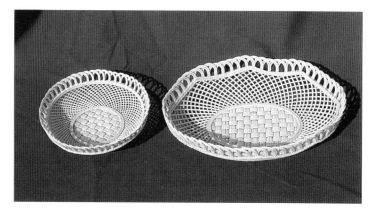

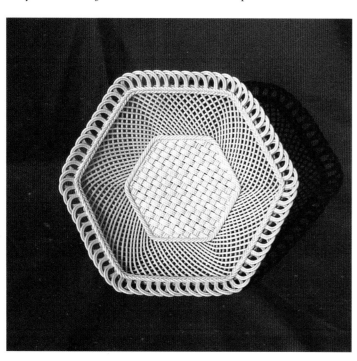

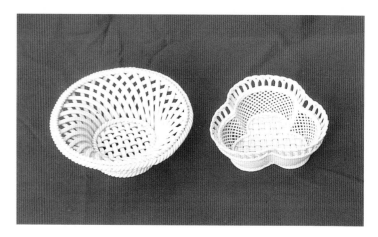

Recorded but not illustrated.

BIRD'S NEST, TRIPLE *(BS.2)*
The same as the single Bird's Nest Basket, three baskets have been joined. Early introduction.
CAKE PLATE, FOOTED *(BS.7)*
CAKE PLATE, FINE EDGE *(BS.10)*
CAKE PLATE, TWIG HANDLED *(BS.12)*
CARD BASKET *(BS.13)*
Round Basket with large looped edge, small flowers on the base of the basket as well as the edge.
CONVOLVULUS BASKET *(BS.15)*
Round, small. It is a larger version of Bird's Nest Basket with looped edge and convolvulus flowers applied.
FLOWERED JEWEL STAND *(BS.18)*
HAWTHORN BASKET 8″ *(BS.21)*.
Like the Forget-me-not Basket, with larger looped edge and more flowers on the edge.
SMALL HEART BASKET *(BS.23)*
HENSHALL'S TWIG, FOOTED *(BS.30)*
HEXAGON WOVEN FRUIT BASKET *(BS.35)*
NO. 5 FOOTED BASKET *(BS.40)*
Smaller version of Italian Flat Twig Basket.
OVAL SCALLOPED, FLAT ROD *(BS.51)*
ROUND BASKET, FLAT LOOPED EDGE *(BS.58)*
ROUND COVERED BASKET, UNFLOWERED *(BS.59)*
ROUND COVERED BASKET, FLAT ROD *(BS.60)*
ROUND BASKET, CENTRE HANDLE NO F1 *(BS.65)*
SHAMROCK BASKET FLAT ROD *(BS.69)*
Small and medium size, Early Basket, same shape as the now-familiar Shamrock Baskets but plain.
SHAMROCK BASKET, LARGE *(BS.70)*
SHAMROCK UNFLOWERED, LARGE *(BS.73)*
SPIDER WEB CAKE PLATE *(BS.74)*.
TRAY, HEXAGONAL WOVEN *(BS.82)*
TRAY, OBLONG WITH TWIG HANDLES *(BS.83)*

TWIG SPECIAL BASKET *(BS.84)* [Top]
Rare, first period 2 strand basket. These 2 strand baskets were made during the first period only until the reintroduction in 1991. *From the late Pat Campbell's collection.*

SYDENHAM TWIG BASKET *(BS.75)* [Above]
An exceptionally rare 2 strand basket. *From the Birks Museum's collection.*

CHAPTER VI
Candlesticks and Lamps

T HE Belleek 'lighting' range is quite small but varied and includes a number of finely crafted candelabra, oil lamps and a nightlight as well as candlesticks and extinguishers. The Cherub candelabra has stood the test of time and has been made in small quantities throughout most periods, though it is quite difficult to find early examples in good condition. In the 1870s these were being sold for around 30/–.

The two oil lamps demonstrate Belleek designers' versatility in uniting parts of other pieces to form a completely new piece, both having the same base but different 'oil wells'.

The range of candlesticks is quite wide comprising the large Gothic, Piano, Thorn, Boy on Dolphin, and Boy and Vine Candlesticks together with the small Boudoir and the Alling-ham candlesticks. Of these the Boy on Dolphin and the Thorn candlestick are the only two which seem to have been re-introduced. There have been other models introduced but they don't seem to have been very popular and were withdrawn.

There are only three recorded candle extinguishers but it is fair to speculate that the Belleek range might have been larger since Derby and particularly Worcester made a wide selection of porcelain extinguishers. Occasionally these extinguishers are mistakenly called snuffs but that name is more correctly applied to the earlier device made of silver or brass, looking a bit like scissors with a special blade, which was used to put out the flame.

BOY CANDELABRA *(CL.13)* [Left]
This candelabra was produced plain white and in at least two colours. It has been made in small quantities throughout most periods.

BOY CANDELABRA *(CL.13)* [Right]
An unusual colouring to this piece.

STAGSHEAD CANDELABRA *(CL.14)* [Opposite]
A unique and magnificent creation typical of Victorian taste, specially commissioned by a Donegal family. *From the Hunt Collection, University of Limerick.*

[Opposite top]
Left to right
IRISH HARP *(MI.44)*
Note the unusual shamrocks which in this instance are applied onto the harp. *From Teresa McHugh and Liz Stillwell's collection.*
BOUDOIR CANDLESTICK *(CL.5)*
Candlestick with applied flowers around the candle holder. Can be found in a coloured version. Very rare.
CORNFLOWER SPILL *(VS.62) From Teresa McHugh and Liz Stillwell's collection.*

[Opposite centre]
SHEPHERD SLEEPING WITH DOG CANDLESTICK *(CL.19)*
From Del Domke's collection.

[Opposite. Bottom left]
CALAWITE CANDLE EXTINGUISHER *(CL.9)*
One of at least three Belleek candle extinguishers for which there is any record. Most candle extinguishers are only marked on the base of the stand so there are probably other Belleek extinguishers in collections which have not been identified as Belleek. This particular one has Belleek's first period mark encircled with Barnicott Banfield & Sydenham trade mark. *Originally from Horace Manning Mann's collection, now part of Mrs McElroy's collection.*

PINEAPPLE GLOBE AMPHORA LAMP *(CL.21)* [Opposite right]
From Del Domke's collection.

AMPHORA LAMP *(CL.22)* [Above]
The body of the Amphora centre piece has been used to make this lamp.

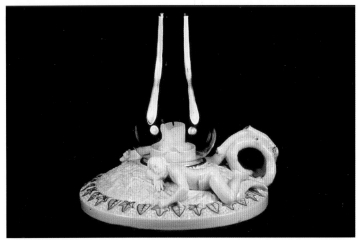

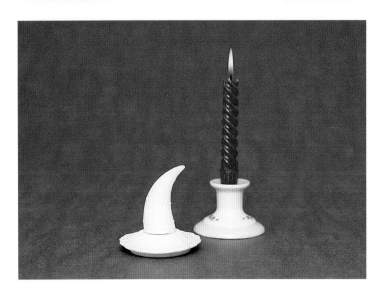

[Above]

DOLPHIN CANDLESTICK *(CL.15)*

Early examples of this are rare but it was reintroduced in 1989.

ANCHORITE CANDLESTICK *(CL.3)*

Not as dainty as the Allingham Candlestick. *From the late Pat Campbell's collection.*

LIGHTHOUSE NIGHTLIGHT HOLDER *(CL.18)* [Below right]
The base of this nightlight is relatively easy to find, but no original tops seemed to have survived the passage of time.

[Above]

BOUDOIR CANDLESTICK *(CL.5)*

[Above]
ART NOUVEAU DISH *(MI.23)*
CANDLE EXTINGUISHER LADY WITH HAT *(CL.11)*
CANDLE EXTINGUISHER GAUNTLET *(CL.10)*
Photograph reproduced by kind permission of The Trustees of the Ulster Museum.

PIANO CANDLESTICK *(CL.20)* [Left]
From Eileen O'Neill's collection.

Recorded but not illustrated

ALLINGHAM CANDLESTICK *(CL.1)*
Gentian flower-shaped candle holder set on leaf base with leaf-stem handle.
BOY AND VINE CANDLESTICK *(CL.7)*
The boy holds a branch which is covered with vine leaves. The same boy seems to have been used to hold the fish spill and the vine comport.
GOTHIC CANDLESTICK *(CL.17)*

Left to right
SHELL MIRROR *(FR.14)*
Large size
BUST OF CLYTIE *(ST.8)*
CORAL MIRROR WITH ORANGE CORAL *(FR.11)*

CHAPTER VII

Mirrors

IT is in these large frames that the fine workmanship of the Belleek artists is shown at its best. With close examination of the flowers one can only marvel at the intricate and delicate work required to make these exquisite flowers.

As might be expected Belleek Frames feature in the Belleek Album; a range of three Lily Frames are illustrated retailing from 12/– to 39/–. In the section of photographs titled 'Paris Exhibition Sample' there is an illustration of a large flower encrusted frame at a price of £7.10.0. This frame has fine examples of roses, chrysanthemum, buddleia, and carnations with coral feet. No size is given but it would seem to be approximately 20″ high. A similar frame is on display in the Belleek Museum.

MIRROR *(FR.4)*
BOUDOIR CANDLESTICK *(CL.5)*

DOUBLE PHOTO FRAME *(FR.3)*

QUEEN VICTORIA MIRROR FRAME *(FR.1)*

Measuring 29″ x 22″, the mirror is believed to have been specially created for Queen Victoria. It passed into the possession of Horace Manning Mann, Houston, Texas, through the generosity of HRH the Duke of Windsor, who was on the Board of Directors of a Canadian oil company with which Horace had connections. Learning of his interest in Belleek, the Duke told him about the mirror which was in the Palace and donated it to Horace. Then, in 1988, at the auction of Mr Mann's collection, Florence Birks bought the mirror for the Birks Museum, Millikin University, Decatur. *From the Birks Museum collection.*

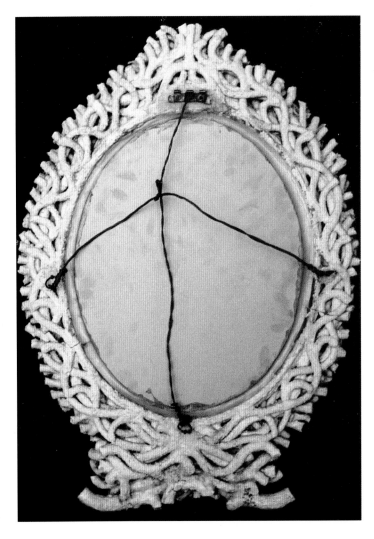

[Top left]
Back view of the Queen Victoria Mirror. It is interesting to see the back view of this mirror, with its coral-like base. Usually mirrors and frames have a solid base on which the flowers are applied.

[Top right]
Close-up view of the top of the mirror. Note the birds on each side of the cross about to fly.

[Above left]
Close-up view of the bottom of the Queen Victoria Mirror with the Harp, Tower and Greyhound.

[Above right]
Another view of the mirror showing in detail some of the most intricate work.

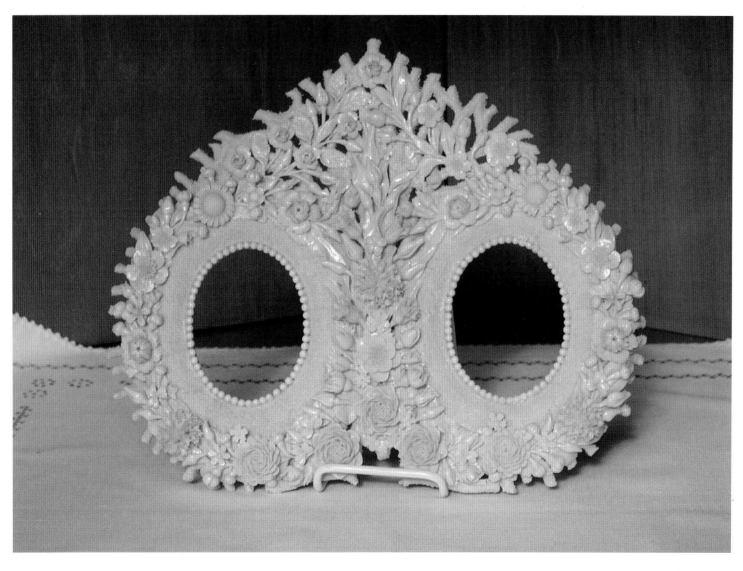

LARGE MIRROR *(FR.2)* [Opposite top]
The history of this mirror is a little hazy compared with Queen
Victoria's mirror. It was purchased in England, and was part of Mrs
McElroy's collection, before being bought by the Belleek Pottery
Limited for their collection. It can now be seen in the Visitors' Centre
at Belleek. Some people believe that these large mirrors were part of
the apprentices' final exam but it is hard to believe that these
beautifully made pieces were the work of inexperienced craftsmen.
From the Belleek Pottery's collection.

[Opposite left]
Close-up views of Belleek's large mirror.

DOUBLE PHOTO FRAME *(FR.3)* [Above]
2nd period. *From Josephine Corriveau's collection.*

[Right, *Left to right*]
LILY OF THE VALLEY PICTURE FRAME *(FR.10)*
LILY OF THE VALLEY MIRROR *(FR.9)*
Both 1st period.

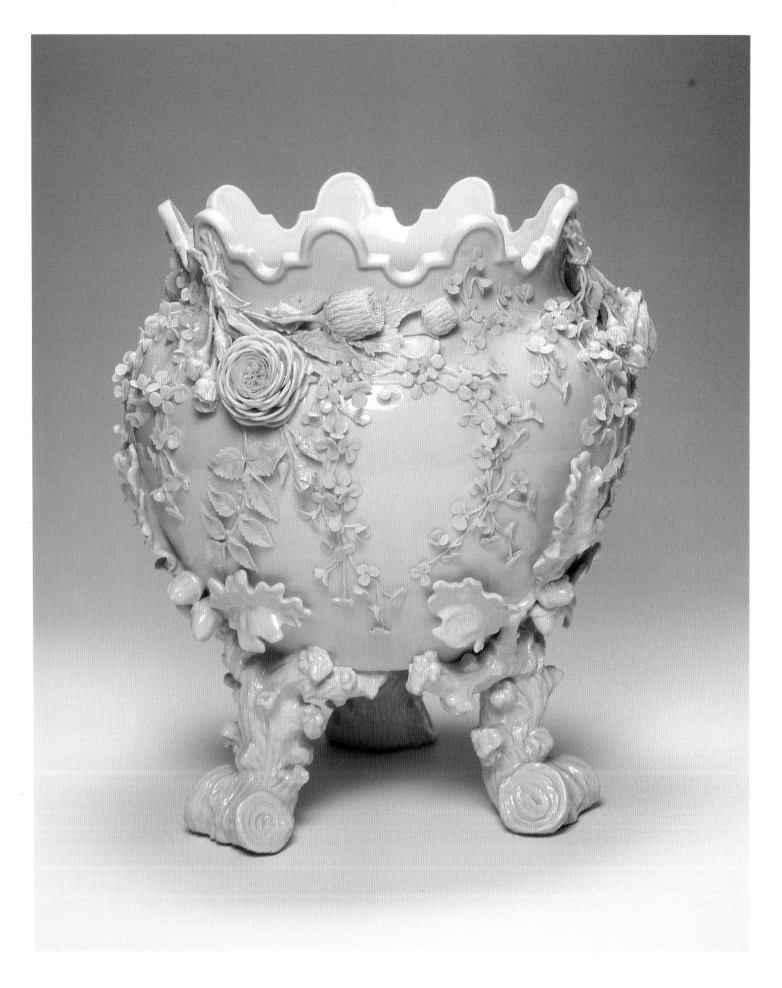

CHAPTER VIII

Jardinières, Flower Pots and Wall Brackets

BELLEEK produced eleven designs of jardinières and most are available footed or unfooted. Apart from the Fern Jardinière, they are very ornate, decorated with birds and applied flowers, and in this day and age do not lend themselves to being used for the purpose for which they were made. However, they suited the taste of the Victorians in whose over-furnished rooms, filled with palms and other plants, these jardinières would certainly have looked magnificent.

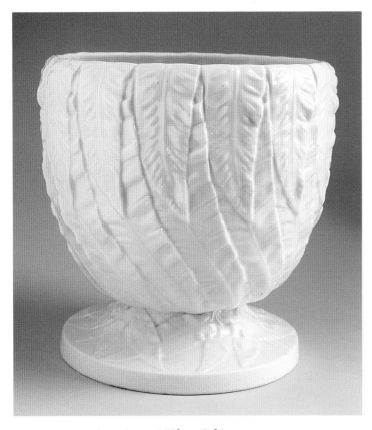

FERN JARDINIÈRE *(FP.20)* [Above left]
An attractive flower pot, though plain for Belleek. Leaf of 'Hart's Tongue' Fern. Available in three sizes.

NAIADS JARDINIÈRE *(FP.31)* [Above right]
Illustrated beside the Prince of Wales Ice Pail. Note the bowl is the same in both. The jardinière comes in two sizes. Tall (13.5″), low (11″).

SHELL JARDINIÈRE *(FP.51)* [Right]
There is also an unfooted version.

OAK JARDINIÈRE *(FP.34)* [Opposite]
From Christine and Peter McCormack's collection.

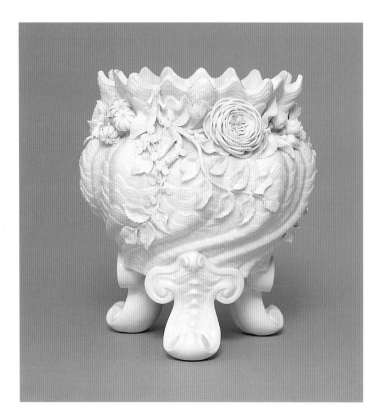

PANEL JARDINIÈRE *(FP.40)* [Above left]
Note the bird perched on the branch. Footed (11″) and unfooted.
THORN JARDINIÈRE *(FP.53)*

ANGEL JARDINIÈRE *(FP.1)* [Above right]
An unusual and rare jardinière. *From Betty and Don Clinton's collection.*

BELLEEK JARDINIÈRE *(FP.4)* [Centre left]
The Belleek jardinière is available footed (10.5″) or unfooted (8″).

LYRE WALL BRACKET *(FP.58)* [Below]
Very rare piece. 1st period
PAIR OF SWANS *(MI.55)*

FINNER JARDINIÈRE *(FP.24)* [Bottom left]
Pair of flower pots illustrating the back and front. Note the 'Harp
handles' the same as used in the jugs. 2nd period

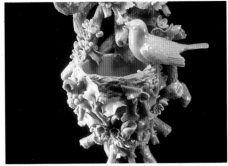

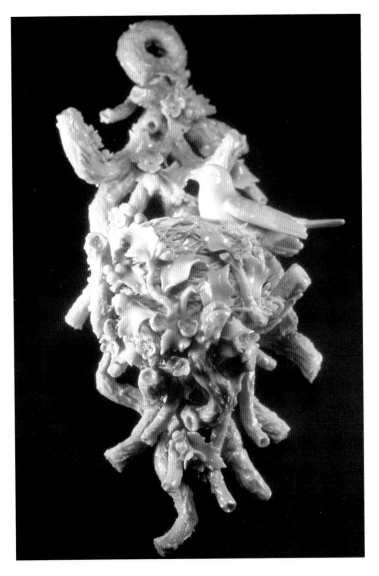

BIRD'S NEST WALL BRACKET *(FP.55)* [Top left]

BIRD'S NEST WALL BRACKET [Top right]
A close-up of the same wall bracket showing the bird perched at the edge of its nest. *From Del Domke's collection.*

[Above, *Left to right*]
BELLEEK FLOWER POT *(FP.11)*
Small size and unflowered.
HENSHALL SPILL *(VS.126)* Flowered
OCTAGON FLOWER POT *(FP.35)* Available in two sizes
DAIL-EIRANN *(MI.41)*
A miniature of the lower house of legislature for Eire.

FRUIT AND VINE LEAF WALL POCKET *(FP.57)* [Centre right]
Although coloured it would appear that the colouring has been added at a later date. 1st period.

[Bottom right, *Left to right*]
CRINKLED FLOWER POT *(FP.17)*
2nd period.
ROOT SPILL SINGLE *(VS.197)*
2nd period.

CHAPTER IX

Lithophanes

LITHOPHANES originated in Europe in the early 19th century. The name is derived from the Greek words *lithos* (stone) and *phane* (appearance). Baron Paul de Bourgoing (1791–1864) developed the process at his porcelain and pottery factory in the village of Rubelles, near Melun. A licence was granted by de Bourgoing to Robert Griffith Jones of Brewer St, London, who took out an English patent (No. 5626) on 13 March 1828. Jones granted a licence to several British potteries, including Belleek.

The process of making lithophane plaques requires the artist to have great technical skill. A positive wax of the subject is carved into a thin sheet of wax mounted onto glass and illuminated from behind to allow the artist to judge the effect of the final product. Then a plaster of Paris mould is made of the wax positive and porcelain paste poured into the mould. This cast is fired at a temperature of 2100 degrees Fahrenheit. About twenty to thirty casts can be made from one mould if care is taken.

It seems that Belleek never designed their own lithophanes but produced them from masters from KPM or PPM of Germany. Belleek lithophanes are always a sepia colour. Some have impressed marks whilst others are not marked at all, which makes dating them very difficult, particularly as the Pottery made them on and off over several periods. They were last reintroduced in 1986.

LOVERS AT TABLE *(LI. 7)* [Opposite]

FARM GIRL WITH GOAT *(LI. 3)* [Right]

GIRL WITH SHAWL LEANING ON BARREL *(LI. 10)* [Left]

CHILD LOOKING IN MIRROR *(LI. 2)* [Above]

LITHOPHANE CREATED DURING ARNOLD'S REIGN *(LI. 11)*

LADIES WITH FAN *(LI.5)*
All the lithophanes are from Mrs McElroy's collection

Recorded – not illustrated

GIRL AT WALL *(LI.4)*
Girl sitting at a wall, shading her eyes and looking into the distance.

CHILD AND OLD MAN WITH HARP *(LI.1)*
A shoeless lass listening to an old man sitting and playing his harp.

LADIES WITH PIGEON *(LI.6)*
One lady holding a pigeon, whilst the other lady looks on.

MADONNA, CHILD AND ANGEL *(LI.8)*
Madonna holding child; angel watches holding small cross.

PRIEST AND ALTAR BOY CROSSING STREAM *(LI.9)*
Both barefooted, the priest holds the altar boy's hand as they prepare to cross the stream. The reflections in the stream are well defined.

CHAPTER X

Holy Water Fonts
and Statues

THIS is one of Belleek's smallest ranges but, in view of the strong Catholic influence in Ireland, it is not surprising that it has been made consistently in small quantities throughout most periods. The Angel and Cross Fonts feature at the end of the Belleek Album.

SACRED HEART FONT *(HO.21)* [Right]
Two sizes. *From Del Domke's collection.*

[Opposite]
ANGEL FONT *(HO.1).*
BLESSED VIRGIN MARY *(HO.8)*
Large size

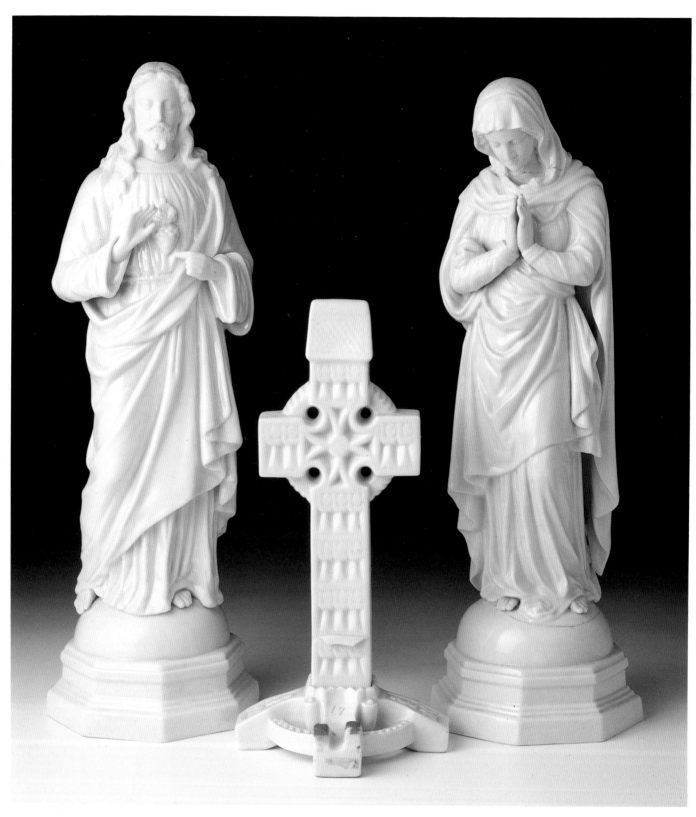

[Above]

SACRED HEART STATUE (*HO.19*)
Two sizes.

CELTIC CROSS AND FONT (*HO.10*)
Holy water stoop missing.

BLESSED VIRGIN MARY (*HO.8*)
Large and small size. *From Graham and Maureen Munton's collection.*

CROSS FONT [Opposite, top left]

ANGEL FONT KNEELING (*HO.5*) [Opposite, top right]
Another piece with close resemblance to Goss's St John's Font. Two sizes. *From Del Domke's collection.*

CHERUB FONT (*HO.14*). [Opposite, bottom]

CHAPTER XI

Jugs

THE large parian jugs made by Belleek were purely decorative in function. The Aberdeen Jug when encrusted with applied flowers is among the most ornate. Coming in three sizes and left- or right-handed, a complete set of six of these jugs is very difficult to obtain but very attractive when achieved. The later Aberdeen Jugs are also available coloured.

The Florence Jug comes in four sizes and is one of the most beautiful jugs Belleek made. The early jugs are particularly fine and are often decorated with pink, turquoise and gilded. The Shell Jug, although rare, is somewhat ungainly. Together with its sugar, also a shell on coral, it depicts a conch shell but is quite impractical.

At the other end of the scale are the little cream jugs with their matching sugar basins. The retail price in the 1870s for these jugs and their sugar basins were from 1/– to 1/6. The range of jugs was quite extensive and available plain, gilded, coloured or both. Some of the jugs were crested.

DIAMOND JUG *(JU.31)* [Opposite]
Unpierced. Very rare. 2nd period.

ABERDEEN JUG *(JU.1)* [Top right]
Pair jugs 2nd. Singles are available, but it is always more difficult to get pairs

ABERDEEN JUG [Right]
Named after Sir James Campbell Hamilton Gordon, 7th Earl and 1st Marquis of Aberdeen, Viceroy of Ireland 1886 and 1905–1915. Available flowered or unflowered. It is probable that the flowered jugs followed on from the unflowered version. Three sizes.

MARINE JUG *(JU.59)* [Top left and above]
Pink, green or white. 2nd period.
From Del Domke's collection.

[Top right]
Left to right
TOY SHELL JUG *(JU.80)* Small size. 1st period.
SCALE JUG *(JU.72)* 2nd period.
LILY JUG *(JU.56)* 2nd period.
TOY SHELL JUG *(JU.80)* 1st period.
ROPE HANDLE JUG *(JU.70)* Rare jug. 1st period.
DOUBLE SHELL JUG *(JU.33)* 2nd period.
RATHMORE JUG *(JU.66)* Two jugs with different finishes.
CLEARY JUG *(JU.28)* 2nd period.
Front, left to right
BOAT JUG *(JU.25)* 2nd period.
LIFFORD JUG *(JU.54)* 2nd period.
BELLEEK POT JUG *(JU.20)* 2nd period.

[Above centre]
Left to right
SHELL JUG *(JU.74)* 1st period.
ABERDEEN JUG *(JU.6)*
Without applied flowers.
SHELL JUG *(JU.74)*
The other side of the same jug. 1st period.

HARP HANDLE JUGS *(JU.49)* [Above]
Available in three sizes, plain, gilded or coloured.

[Above]
Back left to right
CLEARY JUG (*JU.28*)
RATHMORE JUG (*JU.66*)
MASK JUG, TALL (*TMA.18*)
Large. Available in two sizes, 1st period.
Middle row, left to right
FAN JUG (*JU.38*)
Decorated and undecorated. Both 2nd period.
TOY JUG (*JU.79*)
Green trim small size. 1st period.
TOY JUG (*JU.80*)
Large size. 2nd period.
Front row, left to right
LOTUS JUG (*JU.58*)
Note the unusual blue handle. 1st period.
IRISH POT JUG (*JU.53*)
Unusual finish to this popular piece. 1st period.
TOY SHELL JUG (*JU.79*)
Small size. 1st period.

SHELL BUTTER DISHES (*TM.10*) [Right] 3rd period.
MASK JUG (*TMA.18*) Tall and small size.

FLORENCE JUG (*JU.40*) [Right, centre]
The two sides of this jug have different paintings. 1st period. Florence jugs are available in four sizes, and are usually very fine. *From Dr & Mrs Steinberg's collection.* Florence jugs were reintroduced between 1979 and 1983.

TYPHA JUG (*JU.86*). [Above]

[Above]

IRISH POT CREAM (*JU.53*)

DAIRY JUG (*JU.30*)

MASK JUG FOOTED (*JU.60*) [Top and centre left]

Two photos of these jugs showing the mask at the base of the handle. 2nd period. *From the late Pat Campbell's collection.*

LILY SCROLL (*JU.55*) [Above right]

Sometimes called Scroll, it is not plain scroll as it has the detail of small lilies running down the scrolls. 2nd period. *From Eddie Renshaw's collection.*

[Top]
ECHINUS CUP AND SAUCER (TEC.8)
JUG (JU.74)
From Berdell Dickinson's collection.

SHELL CREAM AND SUGAR ON CORAL (JU.74) [Above]
From Betty and Don Clinton's collection.

[Right]
ERNE JUG (JU.36)
FERMANAGH VASE (VS.94)
From Margaret Power's collection

CHAPTER XII

Comports and Dessert Services

DESSERT is the last course of a meal. In former times it was the fifth course at great banquets and was presented in magnificent style.

There is no rule governing what pieces are required to make up a service but generally there is a large centre piece with two high and two low comports and a number of dessert plates. Belleek produced five different dessert services. The largest and most diverse was the Prince of Wales Service.

In the Belleek Album there is a photograph showing a display of the complete service consisting of the Prince of Wales Centre Piece, two Tri-horse Comports and two Tri-dolphin Comports. The plates illustrated with this set are Echinus. (Along with the Echinus footed bowl, on the 5 September 1868 these were the first two pieces from Belleek to be registered at the Board of Trade, London.) The pieces are also illustrated individually along with two other pieces belonging to this service – the Echinus footed bowl which is called a cream bowl

and the Scallop Shell plate. A note of prices alongside these pieces in a pearl finish range as follows: POW CP 105/–, Tri-horse CP 35/–, Tri-dolphin Comport 10/–, the Echinus Plate 21/–, Echinus Cream Bowl 3/6, Scallop Shell 2/–. Gilding, colouring or Bronze finish were considerably more expensive.

The complete Tri-boy Dessert service is also shown with a caption written in Armstrong's hand: 'Dessert Service 27 pieces, 18 Greek pierced Dessert Plates, 4 Tri-boy Comports m/s, 4 Tri-boy Comports tall, 1 Minstrel Centre. Complete, Pearl £21 8.8.'

Two more complete services are shown in this album. The Basket Dessert service with pierced edges and the Greek service both having three sizes of comport and plates to match. Pieces available from these two services are often crested. The Thorn service is not illustrated but came in a range of different colours.

BOY AND SWAN COMPORT *(DS.6)* [Above]
The same comport with a different base and top.

BOY AND SWAN COMPORT *(DS.6)* [Opposite]
From Del Domke's collection.

GREEK PLATE *(DS. 17)* [Top]
Painted by Eugine Sherrin and signed on the front.

[Top right]
Close-up view of the back of the plate showing the mark and name of
the picture.

GREEK PLATES *(DS. 17)* [Above]
Many of these sets were made to order and are often found with
monograms and coats of arms.

TRI-BOY COMPORT *(DS. 25)* Large size [Bottom right]

[Top]
TRI-BOY COMPORT *(DS. 27)*
Low size. 1st period.
TRI-BOY COMPORT *(DS. 26)* Middle size. 1st period.

[Centre left]
TRI-BOY COMPORT *(DS. 25)* Large size.
1st period.
BOY BOMBINEER PIERCED *(DS. 7)*

[Above right]
DOLPHIN AND SHELL COMPORT *(DS. 8)*
An attractive low comport.
DOLPHIN AND SHELL PLATE *(DS. 10)*.

TRI-BOY COMPORT *(DS. 27)* [Left]
Low size. 1st period.

TRI-DOLPHIN LOW COMPORT *(DS.31)* [Top]
Delicately coloured comport.

BASKET DESSERT SERVICE [Above]
High Comport *(DS.1)*, Low Comport *(DS.2)*, with Plates *(DS.4)*.
These Basket services were often made to order.

TRI-DOLPHIN COMPORT HIGH *(DS.30)* [Right]

BITTERN COMPORT *(DS.5)*
Photograph reproduced by kind permission of the Trustees of the Ulster
Museum.

SELECTION OF CRESTED MINIATURES
All second period.

CHAPTER XIII

Crested

ADOLPHUS Goss, the eldest son of William Henry Goss who had founded the Goss Pottery in 1858, was responsible for the introduction of Crested China. When Adolphus Goss put forward his idea to his father he was disappointed to find his father did not share his enthusiasm. Despite this, Adolphus succeeded in getting the small pieces made and crested. The success of the project was so great that production of crested china soon entirely replaced the production of all

other Goss wares and within five years the floor space of the building had been trebled to cope with demand.

In the circumstances, since Belleek gained so much from Goss, it is not surprising that it also followed them into the crested market. All Belleek crested pieces are hard to find. 2nd period pieces are more common, but very occasionally 1st period pieces turn up.

COLLECTION OF CRESTED MINIATURES
All second period.

[Above]
SELECTION OF CRESTED MINIATURES
All second period.

[Left]
COMMEMORATIVE CUP AND SAUCER
A very rare Commemorative Cup and Saucer. 2nd period. *From the late Pat Campbell's collection.*

[Opposite, top left]
NEPTUNE CUP AND SAUCER
Maxwelltown crest. Second period.

[Opposite, top right]
Mug commemorating George V and Queen Mary's Silver Jubilee.
6 May, 1935 2nd period.

[Opposite, bottom]
MINIATURE CLEARY MUG
Cork International Exhibition 1.

CHAPTER XIV

Tea Sets

THEA Sinensis is the Latin name of the tea tree which, if allowed, can reach a height of 30 feet. Native to Assam, China and Japan. Tea was first brought to Europe by the Dutch in 1610 and to England in 1644. However, it was not until 1865 when tea drinking became so fashionable in Society that tea growing was introduced into Ceylon and India. They are now the largest exporters of tea in the world.

Tea Ware was Belleek's largest range. The déjeuner or cabaret sets were made up of a tray, teapot, cream, sugar and two or four cups and saucers. Some designs only consisted of these pieces but others like the Shamrock were much larger and have been added to in other periods.

The Echinus tea service is the most famous. It was ordered by Queen Victoria for her own use and the Belleek album features a photograph of the 'Echinus déjeuner tea ordered for her Majesty The Queen'. The design of the Echinus tea and breakfast service was registered at the Board of Trade on 22 February 1869 by 'Bob W Armstrong, Melrose, Belleek'. In fact the Artichoke service was the first to be registered, preceding the Echinus by some four months.

ABERDEEN

[Opposite top]
ABERDEEN CUP ONLY (TAB.8), TEAPOT (TAB.3) *Christine & Peter McCormack's Collection.*

ARTICHOKE

[Opposite, bottom]
Left to right, standing
BREAD PLATE (TAR.26), TRAY (TAR.1), SIDE PLATE (TAR.27)
Left to right
CUP, SAUCER (TAR.8) and SIDE PLATE (TAR.27), MILK JUG (TAR.17)

[Top right]
Standing
TRAY, pink highlights and gilded (TAR.1), CUP, SAUCER AND SIDE PLATE, gilded (TAR.8 & TAR.27), CUP AND SAUCER (TAR.8)
From Christine & Peter McCormack's Collection.

[Right]
Left to right
CUP SAUCER (TAR.8), COVERED SUGAR (TAR.22), TEAPOT (TAR.3), CREAM, small (TAR.15) Unusual decoration all 1st period. *From the late Pat Campbell's collection.*

103

CELTIC

[Centre left]
'K' VASE, unusual blue background to the Celtic pattern *(TCE.94)*,
TARA VASE *(TCE.92)*, 'J' VASE *(TCE.93)*
All 3rd period.

[Bottom left]
TARA VASE *(TCE.92)*, ARRAN MOR VASE, large *(TCE.81)*,
CANDLESTICK *(TCE.80)*

BLARNEY

RARE HAND-PAINTED CUP AND SAUCER *(TBL.8)* [Top left]
From Roy Holihead's collection.

'CELTIC' RINGHANDLE

[Top right]
Left to right, standing
BREAD PLATE *(TCE.26)*, SIDE PLATE *(TCE.27)*
Left to right
TEAPOT *(TCE.3)*, BREAKFAST CUP AND SAUCER *(TCE.11)*,
COVERED SUGAR *(TCE.22)*, CREAM *(TCE.15)*
All 3rd period.

[Bottom right]
Standing
BREAD PLATE *(TCE.26)*
Left to right
COFFEE CUP AND SAUCER *(TCE.10)*, COVERED SUGAR
(TCE.22), CREAM *(TCE.15)*, COFFEE POT *(TCE.7)*,
COFFEE CUP AND SAUCER *(TCE.10)*
All 3rd period.

'CELTIC LOW'

[Bottom right]
'J' VASE *(TCE.93)*, FRUIT DISH *(TCE.31)*, LOW CELTIC
SAUCERS *(TCL.8)*
All 3rd period.

[Top right]
Left to right
COVERED SUGAR *(TCL.22)*, CREAM *(TCL.15)*
Both 3rd period.

[Bottom left]
Standing
SIDE PLATE *(TCL.27)*
Left to right
LILY COFFEE CUP AND SAUCER. 2nd period *(THL.10)*,
ECHINUS COFFEE CUP AND SAUCER, crested. 1st period
(TEC.10), NEPTUNE COFFEE CUP AND SAUCER. 2nd period
(TNE.10).

[Top left]
Left to right
CELTIC SPILL 'R' *(TCE.91)*, BREAD PLATE *(TCL.26)*, SAUCER
ONLY *(TCL.8)*, SIDE PLATE *(TCL.27)* The blue decoration is
unusual. *All from Charles Easthope's collection.*

[Centre right]
TEAPOT *(TCL.3)*, SHAMROCK COVERED VEGETABLE DISH
(SHA.46) From the Belleek Pottery's collection.

CELTIC HIGH

[Bottom left]
Standing back
TRIDACNA SIDE PLATE *(TTR.27)*
Left to right
ROPE-HANDLE MUG *(TM.40)*, CUP ONLY *(TCH.8)*, CUSTARD
CUP AND SAUCER *(TM.20)*, LOW LILY SUGAR *(TLL.20)*,
BELLEEK POT CREAM *(JU.20)*

CELTIC, THREE-LEG TEA SET

[Top]
TEAPOT *(TC3.3)*, CREAM *(TC3.15)*, CUP AND
SAUCER *(TC3.8)*. *From Roy Holihead's collection.*

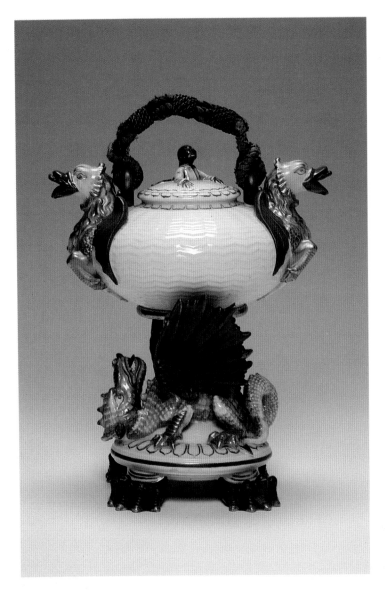

CHINESE TEA WARE

LARGE KETTLE ON STAND. 1st period *(TCH.100)* [Above]. *From Christine & Peter McCormack's collection.*

[Opposite, bottom right]
Standing
TRAY *(TCH.1)*
Left to right
CREAM, small *(TCH.15)*, SUGAR, small *(TCH.20)*, TEAPOT, small *(TCH.4)*, CUP AND SAUCER *(TCH.8)*, TEAPOT, large *(TCH.2)*, CUP AND SAUCER *(TCH.8)*
All first period.

[Opposite, centre right]
Standing
SIDE PLATE *(TCH.27)*
Left to right
SLOP *(TCH.24)*, CREAM, large *(TCH.17)*, TEAPOT, middle *(TCH.3)*, CREAM, medium *(TCH.16)*, SUGAR, small *(TCH.20)*

CONE

[Top right]
Left to right
TEAPOT *(TCO.3)*, CUP AND SAUCER, white *(TCO.8)*, KETTLE, green trim *(TCO.5)*. Note the spout of the kettle has been reduced.
Front
SUGAR BUTTERSCOTCH *(TCO.20)*, CREAM *(TCO.15)*

[Centre right]
TRAY *(TCO.1)*, TEAPOT *(TCO.3)*, SUGAR *(TCO.20)*, CUP AND SAUCER *(TCO.8)*. *From Gene Krach's collection.*

[Bottom right]
Standing
TRAY *(TCO.1)*
Left to right
CUPS AND SAUCERS *(TCO.8)*, TEAPOT *(TCO.3)*, CREAM *(TCO.15)*, SUGAR *(TCO.20)* *From Josephine Corriveau's collection.*

ECHINUS

[Above]
Standing
TRAY *(TEC.1)*
Back
CUP AND SAUCER, pink trim *(TEC.8)*, SUGAR SIFTER
(TEC.52), TEAPOT, gold trim, small *(TEC.4)*, TEAPOT, medium
(TEC.3), SLOP *(TEC.24)*
Front
BREAKFAST CUP AND SAUCER *(TEC.11)*, COFFEE CUP, special
order with family crest *(TEC.10)*, CREAM, large *(TEC.16)*

[Top right]
Top back
SLOP, 1st period *(TEC.24)*, TEAPOT, pink trim, small *(TEC.4)*
Both 2nd period.
Left to right
SUGAR, large *(TEC.21)*, KETTLE, large *(TEC.5)*, TEAPOT, small,
white with gold trim *(TEC.4)*
All 1st period.

[Centre right]
Standing
BREAD PLATE, plain and gilded 9.5″ *(TEC.26)*. All 1st and
impressed. KETTLE, large *(TEC.5)*, CUP AND SAUCER, pink trim
(TEC.8)

[Bottom right]
Standing
TRAY *(TEC.1)*
Left to right
CREAM, large *(TEC.16)*, SUGAR, large *(TEC.21)*, TEAPOT, small
(TEC.4), CUPS AND SAUCERS *(TEC.8)*

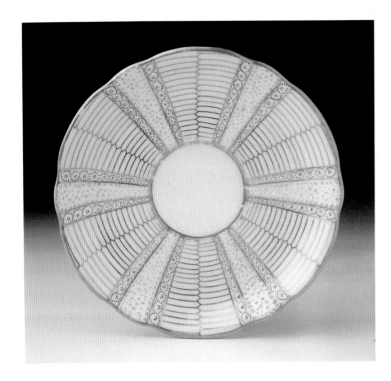

BREAD PLATE, 1st period *(TEC.26)* [Top left]
View of the back of the plate showing the special mark [Centre right]
Close-up of the mark. 'For John Mortlock 204 Oxford Street London'
[Top right]

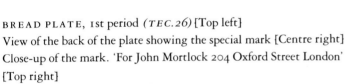

[Centre right]
Left to right
SLOP *(TEC.24)*, TEAPOT, large *(TEC.2)*,
CREAM, large, notice the Crest *(TEC.16) From Margaret Power's collection.*

[Right]
Standing
TRAY *(TEC.1)*
Left to right
MUFFIN DISH *(TEC.35)*, KETTLE, small
(TEC.6), TEAPOT, middle *(TEC.3)*, SLOP
(TEC.24)
Second row
SUGAR, small *(TEC.20)*, CUP AND SAUCER
(TEC.8), SIDE PLATE *(TEC.27)*, CREAM,
small *(TEC.15)*, CUP AND SAUCER *(TEC.8)*,
SIDE PLATE *(TEC.27)*. The green trim on this
set is very rare on Echinus. *From Christine and Peter McCormack's collection.*

ERNE

[Top left]

TRAY (*TER.1*), TEAPOT (*TER.3*), CREAM (*TER.15*), SUGAR (*TER.20*)

[Centre left]

TRAY (*TER.1*), TEAPOT (*TER.3*), CREAM (*TER.15*), SUGAR (*TER.20*), SIDE PLATE (*TER.27*)

The pink tint on this set appears to be a later addition.

[Top right]

CREAM (*TER.15*), SUGAR (*TER.20*)

Standing

SIDE PLATE (*TER.27*), CUP AND SAUCER (*TER.8*) Pottery 'pinking' to this set.

FAN

[Left]

Standing

TRAY (*TFA.1*)

Left to right

CUPS AND SAUCERS (*TFS.8*), TEAPOT (*TFA.3*), CREAM (*TFA.15*), COVERED SUGAR (*TFA.22*), TUMBLER, size 1 (*TFA.57*)

[Bottom right]

TUMBLER, six sizes, 3rd period (*TFA.57*), MINIATURE JUG, 2nd period (*TFA.17*)

FINNER WARE

[Top]

TRAY *(TFI.1)*, TEAPOT *(TFI.3)*, CREAM, small *(TFI.15)*,
SUGAR, small *(TFI.20)*, CUP AND SAUCER *(TFI.8)* All 2nd
period. *From Beverly Poole and Chris Marvell's collection.*

[Above]

Left to right

NEPTUNE CUP AND SAUCER *(TNE.8)*, FINNER CUP AND
SAUCER *(TFI.8)*, NEPTUNE CUP AND SAUCER, decorated
(TNE.8) From Margaret Power's collection.

FIVE O'CLOCK TEA SET

[Centre right]

TRAY *(T50.1)*, TEAPOT *(T50.3)*, CUP AND SAUCER *(T50.8)*,
CREAM *(T50.15)*, SUGAR, 2nd period *(T50.20)*

[Right]

TRAY *(T50.1)*

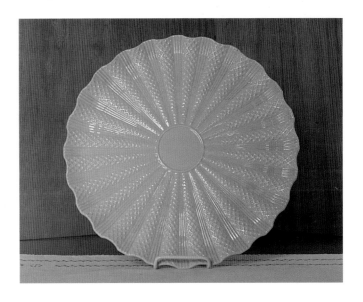

GRASS

[Top left]
Standing
BREAD PLATE *(TGR.26)*
Left to right
TEAPOT STAND *(TGR.40)*, CUP AND SAUCER *(TGR.8)*,
KETTLE *(TGR.5)*, CREAM, small *(TGR.15)*, COVERED SUGAR,
large *(TGR.22)*
All 1st period.

[Top right]
Standing
BREAD PLATE *(TGR.26)*, SAUCER WITH BREAKFAST CUP
(TGR.11)
Left to right
TEAPOT, large with McBirney Teapot lid giving the recipe for
making tea *(TGR.2)*, KETTLE *(TGR.5)*, HONEY POT ON THREE
FEET *(TGR.36)*, CUP AND SAUCER *(TGR.8)*
Front
SUGAR, medium *(TGR.21)*, CREAM, small *(TGR.15)*

[Bottom left]
Standing
TRAY *(TGR.1)*
Left to right
KETTLE *(TGR.5)*, SAUCER ONLY, note colouring *(TGR.8)*,
SUGAR, uncovered, large *(TGR.22)*, CREAM, large *(TGR.17)*,

[Bottom right]
Back, left to right
LIMPET COFFEE CUP AND SAUCER *(TLI.10)*, MASK BREAD
PLATE *(TMA.26)*
Middle row, left to right
IVY SUGAR, middle size *(TIV.21)*, NEPTUNE SUGAR, small size,
note the decoration *(TNE.20)*, CARDIUM ON CORAL *(VS.40)*,
GRASS MILK JUG *(TGR.18)*
Front row, left to right
BOAT JUG *(JU.25)*, MCBIRNEY SWEET DISH *(MI.90)*, RIBBON
SUGAR AND JUG *(JU.68)*, EGG CUP, with shamrock decoration
(THE.48), EGG CUP, with a coral stem *(TEC.48)*

HEXAGON

HAND-PAINTED TRAY, originally from Horace Mann's collection (*THE.1*) [Top right] *From Graham and Maureen Munton's collection.*

[Bottom right]
TRAY (*THE.1*), TEAPOT (*THE.3*), CUP AND SAUCER (*THE.8*), CREAM (*THE.15*), SUGAR (*THE.20*)
All 2nd period.

[Bottom left]
Standing
TRAY (*THE.1*), CUP AND SAUCER (*THE.8*)
Left to right
CUP AND SAUCER (*THE.8*), SUGAR (*THE.20*), CREAM (*THE.15*), KETTLE (*THE.5*), TEAPOT (*THE.3*)
All 2nd period.

[Top left]
Back, left to right
SHAMROCK MOUSTACHE CUP AND SAUCER (*SHA.12*),
TRIDACNA MOUSTACHE CUP AND SAUCER (*TTR.12*)
Front, left to right
GRASS MOUSTACHE CUP AND SAUCER (*TGR.12*), HEXAGON MOUSTACHE CUP (*THE.12*), RING-HANDLE MOUSTACHE CUP AND SAUCER (*TRI.12*) These cups are difficult to find and much sought after. *From Graham and Maureen Munton's collection.*

Selection of painted Hexagon teaware [Above]. All 2nd period.

BREAD PLATE, hand-painted *(THE.26)* [Left] *From Jan Golaszewski's collection.*

[Opposite centre left]
Left to right
CUP AND SAUCER, butterscotch *(THE.8)*, CREAMS, green and white with gold trim *(THE.15)*, TEAPOT, pink *(THE.3)*
All 2nd period.

[Opposite bottom left]
CUP AND SAUCER *(THE.8)*, SIDE PLATE, hand-painted and signed *(THE.27)*

[Top]
Standing
TRAY, oval hexagon tray, a rare shape *(THE.101)*, SIDE PLATE *(THE.27)*
Left to right
KETTLE *(THE.5)*, SUGAR *(THE.20)*, TEAPOT *(THE.3)*
Front
COFFEE CUP *(THE.10)*, CREAM *(THE.15)*
Standing front
LEAF PLATE *(MI.84) From Roy Holihead's collection.*

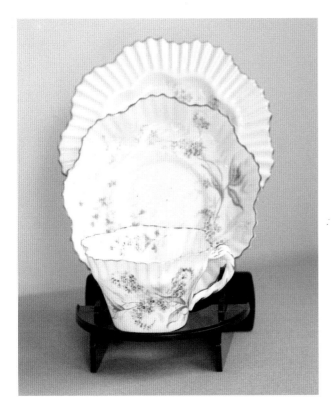

INSTITUTE WARE

[Top left]
Standing, left to right
BREAD PLATE *(TIN.26)*, SIDE PLATE *(TIN.27)*, SAUCER WITH
BREAKFAST CUP, with gold trim *(TIN.11)*
Left to right
BREAKFAST CUP AND SAUCER *(TIN.11)*, COVERED SUGAR
(TIN.22), CREAM *(TIN.15)*

[Above]
Left to right
SLOP *(TIN.24)*, SAUCER ONLY *(TIN.8)*, CREAM, note the sea
horse handle *(TIN.15)*

[Top right]
Standing
PLATE 10″, *(TIN.30)*, BREAKFAST SAUCER AND CUP
(TIN.11), SUGAR *(TIN.20)*

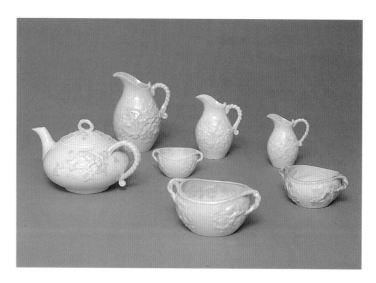

IVY

LACE

[Above]
Back, left to right
JUG, large (*TIV.19*), JUG, medium (*TIV.18*), JUG, small (*TIV.17*)
Front, left to right
TEAPOT (*TIV.3*), SUGAR, small (*TIV.22*), SUGAR, large
(*TIV.20*), SUGAR, medium (*TIV.21*)

[Top left]
Left and right
LIMPET CUP AND SAUCER (*TLI.8*), TEAPOT (*TLA.3*), LIMPET
CUP AND SAUCER, footed (*TLI.8*)
From Josephine Corriveau's collection.

[Centre left]
CUP AND SAUCER, footed cup (*TLA.8*), SIDE PLATE (*TLA.27*),
CUP, cob trim (*TLA.8*), SIDE PLATE, gold trim (*TLA.27*)

[Top right]
TRAY (*TLA.1*) Another version of decoration to the Lace Tray. *From
Berdell Dickinson's collection.*

[Bottom right]
CUP AND SAUCER, unfooted (*TLA.8*), SIDE PLATE, gold
decoration (*TLA.27*)

[Above]
TRAY AND SAUCER (*TLA.1*) Showing the variations of colours
which was used to give individual patterning on sets.
From Dr and Mrs Steinberg's collection.

[Left]
FOOTED SUGAR (*TLA.20*), FOOTED CREAM (*TLA.15*)
Both 2nd period.

HIGH LILY

Not to be confused with Low Lily, which is totally different.

[Top]
TRAY *(THL.1)*, TEAPOT *(THL.3)*, CUP AND SAUCER *(THL.8)*,
CREAM *(THL.15)*, SUGAR *(THL.20) From Josephine Corriveau's
collection.*

[Centre right]
COFFEE CUP AND SAUCER *(THL.10)*, CUP AND SAUCER
(THL.8) Both 2nd period. *From Christine & Peter McCormack's collection.*

[Right]
LIMPET CUP TRAY *(TLI.63)*, HIGH LILY CUP TRAY *(THL.63)*

LOW LILY

[Above]
CUP AND SAUCER *(TLL.8)*, TEAPOT *(TLL.3)*, CREAM, small
(TLL.15), SUGAR, small *(TLL.20)*
From Josephine Corriveau's collection.

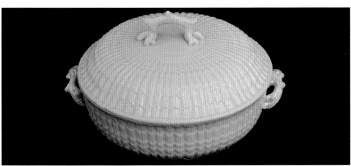

LIMPET

COVERED VEGETABLE DISH *(TLI.45)* [Above]
From Dr Robert E. Gregg's collection.

[Top left]
CUP AND SAUCER *(TLI.8)*, SIDE PLATE, with cob finish
(TLI.27) All 3rd period.

[Top right]
Left to right
BREAD PLATE, standing *(TLI.26)*, CUP AND SAUCER *(TLI.8)*,
KETTLE *(TLI.5)*. *From Berdell Dickinson's collection.*

[Centre right]
Left to right
KETTLE, large *(TLI.5)*, COFFEE POT *(TLI.7)*, TEAPOT,
medium, on feet *(TLI.3)*
Second row
SUGAR *(TLI.20)*, CUP AND SAUCER *(TLI.8)*, CREAM,
small *(TLI.15)*, CREAM, large, on feet *(TLI.16)*, CUP AND
SAUCER, on feet *(TLI.8)*
From Peter and Christine McCormack's collection.

[Above]
Back, left to right
BREAD PLATES *(TLI.26)*, COFFEE POT *(TLI.7)*, PLATE, 7",
with view of the Pottery *(TLI.28)*. All 3rd period.
Second row, Left to right
MILK JUG, large 3rd green *(TLI.19)*, TRIDACNA MILK JUG, 3rd
black *(TTR.17)*, TEAPOT, large, unusual colouring, 2nd green,
reputed to have come from Cyril Arnold's collection *(TLI.2)*,
TEAPOT, middle size, 2nd green *(TLI.3)*
Front row
CREAM *(TLI.15)*, CUP AND SAUCER *(TLI.8)*, SIDE PLATE
(TLI.27), CEREAL BOWL AND PLATE *(TLI.41)*

MASK

[Top left]
Back
COFFEE POT *(TMA.7)*, SUGAR, small *(TMA.20)*,
TEAPOT, small *(TMA.3)*, JUG, tall *(TMA.17)*, CREAM,
low *(TMA.15)*
Front
CUP AND SAUCER *(TMA.8)* All 3rd period.
From Dr Robert E. Gregg's collection.

[Above]
TRIDACNA CUP AND SAUCER *(TTR.8)*, FAN CUP AND
SAUCER *(TFA.8)*, MASK CUP AND SAUCER, two very unusual and
rare cups and saucers *(TMA.8) From Fred and Betty Gary's collection.*

POWDER BOWL *(TMA.70)* [Top right]
From Christine and Peter McCormack's collection.

CUP AND SAUCER *(TNE.8)* 2nd period

NEPTUNE

[Top]

Back, left to right

CREAM, large *(TNE.16)*, TEAPOT *(TNE.3)*

Second row, left to right

LIP SALVE *(TNE.69)*, TRIDACNA SUGAR *(TTR.22)*, CUP AND
SAUCER, butterscotch *(TNE.8)*

Front

COFFEE CUP AND SAUCER, butterscotch *(TNE.10)*,
CREAM, large *(TNE.16)*

[Centre right]

TRAY *(TNE.1)*, TEAPOT *(TNE.3)*, CREAM *(TNE.15)*,
SUGAR *(TNE.20)*, CUPS AND SAUCERS *(TNE.8)*
All second period.

[Right]

Left to right

BAMBOO TEAPOT, large *(TM.63)*, NEPTUNE CREAM, small
(TNE.15), NEPTUNE CREAM, large *(TNE.16)*, NEPTUNE SLOP,
low *(TNE.24)*, CARDIUM ON SHELL *(VS.36)*, CARDIUM ON
SHELL *(VS.35)*

RING HANDLE

Part of a large breakfast service especially commissioned by Dr O. Ternan and painted by Eugine Sherrin. Dr O. Ternan was a patron of Belleek. Each piece has a named Irish scene and is signed.
BREAKFAST CUP AND SAUCER *(TRI.11)* [Centre left] A rare view of the River Erne, looking east upstream, before the character of the river was changed by the drainage scheme.
The complete service is from Mrs McElroy's collection.

[Top left]
Standing
BREAD PLATE, Glenveigh Castle, Donegal *(TRI.26)*, SIDE PLATE, Cromwell Bridge, Killarney *(TRI.27)*, SAUCER, Tully Castle *(TRI.8)*
Left to right
EGG CUPS *(TRI.48)*, MUFFIN DISH *(TRI. 35)*, CUP, Glengarriff Cork *(TRI.8)*

[Centre right]
BREAKFAST CUP, near Cliff on Erne *(TRI.11)*, SAUCER, Barnes Gap, Donegal *(TRI.11)*, SLOP, Dargle Bridge *(TRI.24)*, CREAM, in the Glen on the Downs *(TRI.18)*, TEAPOT, Glendalough *(TRI.3)*

MASONIC BREAKFAST CUP AND SAUCER *(TRI.11)* [Top right] Belleek also produced earthenware services for masonic lodges. 1st period.

[Above]
JUG, medium *(TRI.18)*, JUG, large *(TRI.19)*

[Top left]
Left to right
Collection of Ring-handle cups and saucers with different decorations.

BREAD PLATE *(TRI.26)* [Above] Ringhandle plates with rare
Limoges decoration. 1st period.
Photograph courtesy, the National Museum of Ireland

[Top right]
Standing
BREAD PLATE *(TRI.26)*, COFFEE CUPS AND
SAUCERS *(TRI.10)* Dainty decoration to Ring-handle blanks.
From Eileen O'Neill's collection.

BREAKFAST CUP AND SAUCER *(TRI.11)*. [Centre right]
From Berdell Dickinson's collection.

PLATE *(TRI.28)*. [Right] *From Berdell Dickinson's collection.*

[Top]

COFFEE CUPS AND SAUCERS *(TRI.10)*, CREAM JUG *(TRI.15)*, SUGAR *(TRI.20)* Hand-painted coffee set with different game birds depicted. 3rd period. *From Margaret and Rodney Capper's collection.*

MOUSTACHE CUP AND SAUCER *(TRI.12)* [Left] Apart from being a rare moustache cup and saucer, the decoration is also very unusual. 1st period.

PLATE *(TRI.27)* [Above left] Painted and signed by L. Allingham.

View of the signature [Above right].

THE LIMOGES DECORATION

[Top left]

Back, standing

BREAD PLATE, with Limoges decoration (*TRI.26*)
From Charles Easthope's collection.

Left to right

SLOP, with stork decoration (*TRI.24*), JUG, convolvulus decorated
(*TRI.17*) *Both from Charles Easthope's collection.*

PLATE, part of a breakfast service (*TRI.28*), CUP, showing different
colour decoration (*TRI.8*)

Front

SLOP, with convolvulus decoration (*TRI.24*), CUPS, showing
different colour decoration (*TRI.8*), BREAKFAST CUP AND
SAUCER, saucer matched (*TRI.11*). All 1st period.

COFFEE CUPS AND SAUCERS (*TRI.10*) [Top right] Beautifully
gilded elegant cups and saucers.

BREAKFAST CUP AND SAUCER (*TRI.11*) [Centre right] Limoges
decorated. A rare example of this type. 1st period.

RING-HANDLE CUP, SAUCERS AND SIDE PLATES [Bottom
left] With stork decoration. In Japanese mythology the stork
symbolizes longevity. The back and front decorations are illustrated.
From Mrs McElroy's collection.

Illustrating red 1st marks

BREAKFAST CUP AND SAUCER (*TRI.11*) [Bottom right]
Convolvulus decoration. The convolvulus is a weed known in Ireland
as 'Robin Run the Hedges' as it is so prolific in the hedgerows.

SCROLL

[Top]
Left to right
All Coffee Cups and Saucers
NEPTUNE *(TNE.10)*, SCROLL *(TSC.10)*, LACE *(TLA.10)*,
LIMPET *(TLI.10)*, ECHINUS *(TEC.10)*
From Edith Jacobson's collection.

[Centre left]
Left to right
CREAM *(TSC.15)*, SUGAR *(TSC.20)*
Standing
SIDE PLATE *(TSC.27)*, CUP AND SAUCER *(TSC.8)* All 2nd
period.

SHELL

SHELL BISCUIT JAR *(TSH.39)* [Opposite, right] 1st period

[Opposite, bottom left]
SHELL MUFFINEER *(TSH.52)*, MUSTARD POT, from Ring-handle Cruet *(TRI.53)*, CHURN CRUET WITH SPOON *(TM.18)*, SALT SPOON

BOXED SHELL SALT *(TSH.51)* [Top left] The coral is picked out in pink. The illustrated box was specially made to hold the salts and spoons. 1st Period. *From Liz Stillwell's collection.*

BISCUIT BOX *(TSH.38)* [Above]

[Top right]
Standing
TRAY *(TSH.1)*
Left to right
CUP AND SAUCER *(TSH.8)*, SUGAR COVERED *(TSH.22)*, TEAPOT *(TSH.3)*, CREAM *(TSH.15)* All 1st period

TEAPOT *(TSH.3)* [Right]

[Top]
Standing, left to right
ERNE LEAF PLATE *(MI.76)*, LEAF PLATE *(MI.87)*
Left to right
RIBBON JAM POT *TM.27)*, SHELL MINT DISH *(TSH.76)*,
SHELL SWEET DISH *(TSH.75)*

[Above right]
SALAD SIDE PLATE, hand-painted *(TM.54)*, TRIPLE SHELL
MENU HOLDER *(TSH.56)*

SALAD SIDE PLATE *(TM.54)* [Above left] Hand-painted
From Liz Stillwell's collection.

SYDNEY

THISTLE

[Top]
Left to right
CUP AND SAUCER *(TSY.8)*, TRAY *(TSY.1)*
Sitting on the tray
TEAPOT *(TSY.3)*, CUP AND SAUCER *(TSY.8)*,
CREAM *(TSY.15)*, SUGAR *(TSY.20)*, CUP AND SAUCER *(TSY.8)*

[Left]
TRAY *(TTH.1)*, TEAPOT, gold mark *(TTH.3)*, BREAD PLATE,
gold mark *(TTH.26)*
CUP AND SAUCER *(TTH.8)* Note the different shape of the cup and
saucer. The cup and saucer on the right-hand side is gold mark and has
been remodelled.
CUP AND SAUCER, gold mark *(TTH.8)*
From Dr Robert E. Gregg's collection.

[Above]
TRAY *(TTH.1)*, TEAPOT *(TTH.3)*, SUGAR *(TTH.20)*,
CREAM *(TTH.15)*, CUPS AND SAUCERS *(TTH.8)*
All 1st period.

THORN

JUG, large *(TTO.19)* [Top left]

[Centre left]
Standing
THORN DESSERT PLATES, note colouring and crested *(DS.22)*.
Left to right
TEAPOT, white with cob, small *(TTO.4)* 1st period, CREAM, small
(TTO.15), SUGAR, small *(TTO.20)* THORN DESSERT
COMPORT, matches the plate *(DS.21)*, SCENT *(TTO.68)*, CUP AND
SAUCER, plain *(TTO.8)*, SAUCER, colour variation *(TTO.8)*

THORN KETTLE *(TTO.6)* [Left] 1st period.

[Top right]
MUG *(TTO.13)*, CUP AND SAUCER *(TTO.8)* Both 1st period.

[Above]
Left to right
CELTIC CANDLESTICKS *(TCE.79)* 3rd period, BRUSH TRAY
(TTO.66) 1st period, CANDLESTICKS *(TTO.80)* 1st period.

THORN CANDLESTICKS *(TTO.80)* [Opposite, top left] 1st period

TRIDACNA

[Top right]

TRAY *(TTR.1)*, CUPS AND SAUCERS *(TTR.8)*, KETTLE, small *(TTR.5)*, TEAPOT, small *(TTR.4)*, CREAM, small *(TTR.15)* SUGAR, small unusual decoration *(TTR.20)*. All 1st period.

[Centre]

Left to right

KETTLE, small, gold lines *(TTR.5)* 1st period, KETTLE, large, blue trim *(TTR.6)* 2nd period, TEAPOT, large *(TTR.4)*, TEAPOT, medium, pink trim and gilded *(TTR.3)* 1st period, TEAPOT, small *(TTR.2)*

Front

CREAM, small *(TTR.15)*, SUGAR, small *(TTR.20)*, SUGAR, large *(TTR.21)*, SUGAR, medium covered *(TTR.22)*, SUGAR, small covered *(TTR.23)*, TEAPOT STAND *(TTR.78)*

[Above]

SIDE PLATE *(TTR.27)*

CUP AND SAUCER *(TTR.8)* 1st period. All monogrammed.

[Top]
Standing
BREAD PLATE, pink trim with view of Pottery *(TTR.26)*, SIDE
PLATE *(TTR.27)*
Left to right
KETTLE, blue trim *(TTR.5)*, TEAPOT, small, pink trim *(TTR.4)*,
BREAKFAST CUP AND SAUCER *(TTR.11)* 1st period, MUFFIN
DISH *(TTR.35)*, TEA CUP AND SAUCER *(TTR.8)*, BOAT
SUGAR *(TTR.31)*

[Above]
TRAY, small *(TTR.66)*, TEAPOT, small *(TTR.4)*, CREAM, small
(TTR.15), SUGAR, medium *(TTR.22)*, COFFEE CUP AND
SAUCER *(TTR.10)*. *From Andy and Chuck Oster's collection.*

[Centre right]
Standing
BREAD PLATE *(TTR.26)*, SIDE PLATE *(TTR.27)*
Left to right
CUP AND SAUCER *(TTR.8)*, TEAPOT *(TTR.2)*, CREAM
(TTR.15) All 1st period green. Decorated by Cyril Arnold.
From Murray and Eunice Robinson's collection.

CUP ON TRAY *(TTR.63)* [Bottom right] 2nd period.

[Opposite, top]
Back, left to right
LIMPET COFFEE CUP AND SAUCER *(TLI.10)* 3rd period.
TRIDACNA BREAKFAST CUP AND SAUCER *(TTR.11)*
Front, left to right
TRIDACNA COFFEE CUP AND SAUCER *(TTR.10)*, THISTLE
CUP AND SAUCER *(TTH.8)* Notice the rim of the saucer is turned
down. Later Thistle saucers do not have this feature. 1st period.
LOW LILY CUP AND SAUCER *(TLL.8)*

VICTORIA

CUPS AND SAUCERS *(TVI.8)* [Above]
From Peter and Christine McCormack's collection.

[Left]
Left to right
CUP AND SAUCER *(TVI.8)*, SWAN, large *(MI.55)* ERNE LEAF
PLATE *(MI.78)*. *From Andy and Chuck Oster's collection.*

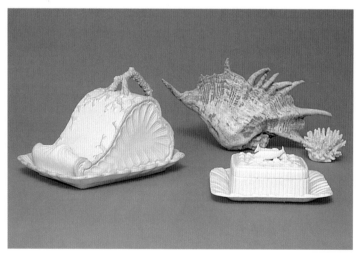

PATTERN X

[Top left]
Standing
BREAD PLATE *(TSX.26)*
Left to right
FLOWERED CUP AND SAUCER. A very unusual shaped cup and
saucer for Belleek, all the more so since the cup has a number and is
unmarked, whilst the saucer is marked with the usual Belleek 1st
period mark *(TSX.8)*. MILK JUG *(TSX.17)*. BREAKFAST CUP
AND SAUCER. The shape of this cup is the same as the flowered cup.
Part of a set which would have been a special order *(TSX.11)*.
From Graham and Maureen Munton's collection.

MISCELLANEOUS

[Left]
CHEESE COVER AND STAND *(TM.15)*, SARDINE BOX AND
STAND *(TM.55)*

[Top right]
RATHMORE BISCUIT JAR *(TM.5)*, MCBIRNEY SWEET DISH
(MI.90)

CRUET *(TM.17)* [Centre right] Three charming little houses, making
up salt, pepper and mustard pots on a tray with their own little spoon.
From Liz Stillwell's collection.

[Above]
SYCAMORE PLATE *(MI.106)*, DIAMOND BISCUIT JAR *(TM.4)*

[Left]
ROUND TUMBLERS, two sizes *(TM. 70/1)*, WINE GLASS, middle size *(TM. 78)*

[Top]
TEAPOT STAND EARTHENWARE *(TM. 60)* Considering a hot teapot would have been placed on this stand, the painting has lasted well, LEAF PLATE *(MI. 86)*, LEAF PLATE *(MI. 85)*, IRISH POT *(VS. 143)*

[Above]
Earthenware plates with a view of the Pottery. (Tea set unrecorded) *From Mrs McElroy's collection.*

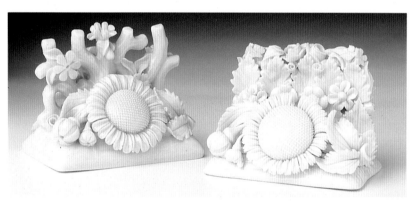

EARTHENWARE TEAPOT STAND *(TM.61)* [Top left] A romantic view of the Donegal Mountains in the background and Donegal Castle which was once the home of the Brookbrough family.

The back of the Teapot stand [Top right], illustrating the unusual blue mark, and the impressed harp.
From Graham and Maureen Munton's collection.

MENU HOLDERS *(TM.36)* [Centre left] Being hand-made, these menu holders are all slightly different. 2nd period.
From Graham and Maureen Munton's collection.

[Left]
BREAD PLATE *(TSX.26)*, CUP AND SAUCER *(TSX.8)*.
From Del Domke's collection.

CUP AND SAUCER *(TSX.8)* [Above] An unusual shaped cup and saucer with flowered 'limoges' decoration. 1st period.
Photograph courtesy the National Museum of Ireland.

PAPAL TIARA CHEESE STAND *(TM.16)* [Opposite, left] 1st period.
Photograph courtesy the National Museum of Ireland.

SHAMROCK

[Top]
Standing
TRAY *(SHA.1)* 2nd period.
Left to right
HONEY POT ON STAND *(SHA.36)* 2nd period, KETTLE, large *(SHA.6)*, BISCUIT BARREL *(SHA.39)* 3rd period.
Front
CREAM, small, flat *(SHA.15)*, SUGAR, small *(SHA.20)*, MARMALADE JAR *(SHA.40)*, TEAPOT, large *(SHA.2)*, CUP AND SAUCER, low *(SHA.8)*.

[Above]
IRISH POT, middle *(VS.143)*, BREAD PLATE, standing *(SHA.26)*, TEAPOT, large *(SHA.2)*, IRISH CREAM *(JU.53)*.

KETTLE *(SHA.6)* [Top left]

Mark of the above kettle [Above] 1st period which is very rare.

[Top right]
MARMALADE BARREL *(SHA.37)*, PLATE *(SHA.28)*, TRINKET BOX *(SHA.72)*, CUP ON TRAY *(SHA.63)*, JAM JAR. Note the different decoration with the lid silvered *(SHA.38)*.

[Centre right]
Back
MILK JUG *(SHA.17)*, JAM JAR *(SHA.38)* 3rd period
Front
HARP SHAMROCK PEPPER 1st period *(SHA.54)*, TOY SHAMROCK CREAM, note pink colouring *(SHA.15)* 1st period, MUG, crested *(SHA.13)* 2nd period.

[Right]
Back
COFFEE POT *(SHA.7)*
Left to right
COFFEE CUPS AND SAUCERS *(SHA.10)*, SUGAR *(SHA.20)*, CREAM *(SHA.15)* Although not Shamrock, Shamrock blanks have been used and over-painted with flowers.

[Top]
Left to right
TRAY (SHA.1) 2nd period, CREAM, small, flat (SHA.15), SUGAR, small (SHA.20), TEAPOT, large (SHA.2), COFFEE CUPS AND SAUCERS (SHA.10).

[Above]
SIDE PLATE (SHA.27), PLATE 7″ (SHA.28), PLATE 8″ (SHA.29), CUP AND SAUCER, tall (SHA.9), CUP AND SAUCER, low shape (SHA.8).

EGG HOLDER (SHA.47) [Above] Not strictly Shamrock, but has the basket background.

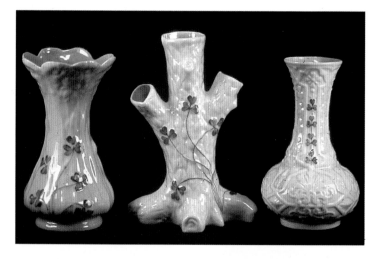

OTHER SHAMROCK PIECES

PIERCED TUB VASE *(SHA.84)* [Above]

ART NOUVEAU BUTTER PLATE *(MI.23)* [Left]

[Top right]
ONION BASE SPILL VASE *(SHA.87)*, TREE-STUMP VASE
(SHA.83), SPILL VASE *(SHA.85)*

ASHTRAYS DIFFERENT DESIGNS *(SHA.79)* [Centre right]

PIERCED VASE *(SHA.88)* [Top left]

TYPHER JUG *(JU.86)* [Opposite, left]

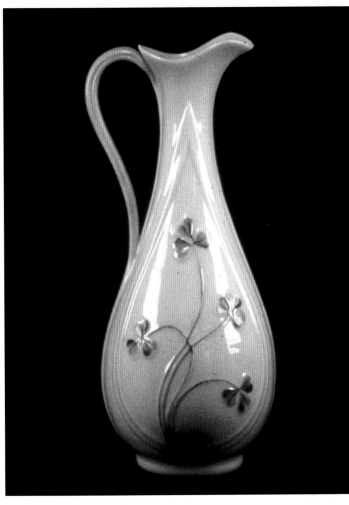

HARP SHAMROCK

[Top]
Standing
BREAD PLATE (*SHP.26*)
Left to right
CRUET (*SHP.54*), TEAPOT (*SHP.3*), SUGAR (*SHP.20*), CREAM
(*SHP.15*)
Front
CUP AND SAUCER (*SHP.8*)

[Above]
Left to right, back row
CHURN CRUET (*TM.18*), PRIMROSE PLATE (*MI.100*), HARP
SHAMROCK CRUET. (*SHP.54*) These are often not marked, which
is understandable because there is so little room for the mark.
Front
THORN BELL (*TTO.70*), SHELL SALT (*TSH.51*), SALT WITH
SPOON (*TM.42*), MENU HOLDER, flowered (*TM.36*)

CHAPTER XV

Christmas Plates

THE first Christmas plate was introduced in 1970, the brainchild of the General Manager, Tommy Campbell. Impressed by the work done by the Kilkenny Design Centre, Tommy commissioned Jim Kirkwood to design a plate for Belleek.

From 1970 to 1976 there was no specific theme to the design on the plates. Castlecaldwell, the ancestral home of John Bloomfield, was depicted on the first plate. Then from 1977 to 1983 the Irish Fauna series was introduced, again designed by Jim Kirkwood. In 1978 it was planned to have a dormouse; the adverse reaction to this idea caused it to be changed to a salmon.

From 1984 to 1987 the theme was Irish Flora, designed by Wendy Walsh, a leading Irish artist who specialised in botanical subjects. This series differed from the previous series. In the past the plates had been modelled in relief; now a colour transfer print was used.

In 1988 the distinctively modelled plate which had been used from the inception of the idea was changed to the 7″ Holly plate with a transfer centre. The only difference from year to year would be the central theme.

In 1991 the series Irish Christmas Scenes of 100 years ago was introduced. This series will probably continue until 1994.

CHRISTMAS PLATES 1970–1975 *(30.b)* [Opposite top]
1970 Calstlecaldwell
1971 Celtic Cross
1972 Wild Geese – symbolising emigration.
1973 Drumcliff Church – The burial place of William Butler Yeats
1974 Devenish Island – An early monastic settlement in Co. Fermanagh
1975 Celtic Cross

CHRISTMAS PLATES 1976–1981 *(31.b)* [Opposite centre]
1976 Dove   1979 The Irish Hare
1977 Robin   1980 Hedgehog
1978 The Salmon   1981 The Red Squirrel

CHRISTMAS PLATES 1982–1985 *(32.b)* [Opposite bottom]
1982 The Seal   1984 Irish Whitebeam
1983 The Red Fox   1985 Irish Heather

CHRISTMAS PLATES 1986–1990 *(33.b)* [Above]
1986 Irish Wild Rose   1989 Doorway Scene
1987 Irish Fleabane   1990 Santa Claus
1988 Window Scene

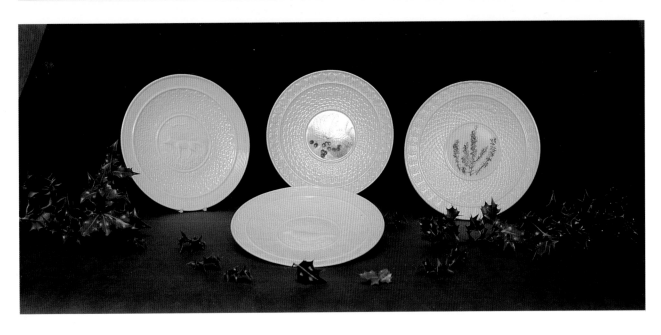

After Word

Nᴏᴛ all collections need to be unique to be of value or
worthy of note. Yan Golaszewski, having always had a
passion for decorative plates, started his collection with Belleek
Christmas plates. From this small start he progressed to Bread
Plates and saucers of which he has thirty-seven.

NEPTUNE BREAD PLATE *(TNE.26)* [Top left] 2nd period

GRASS BREAD PLATE *(TGR.26)* [Centre left] 2nd period

ECHINUS BREAD PLATE *(TEC.26)* [Bottom left] 2nd period

LIMPET BREAD PLATE *(TLI.26)* [Bottom centre] 2nd period

THORN BREAD PLATE *(TTO.26)* [Top right] 2nd period

SHAMROCK BREAD PLATE *(SHA.26)* [Bottom right] 2nd period

BOY WITH FISH SPILL *(VS. 22)* THORN PLATE *(DS. 22)*

Tea Sets

ABERDEEN

Probably named after James Campbell Hamilton Gordon, 7th Earl & Marquis of Aberdeen, Viceroy of Ireland in 1886. His wife, Lady Aberdeen was a promoter of the Arts.
Colour Ways: Plain white with cob highlights and blue trim.
Period 2nd.

ARTICHOKE

Mrs Armstrong, wife of Robert William Armstrong, one of the Founders and first Manager of the Pottery, is credited for the design of this set.
Colour Ways: White, white with gilding, green with gilding, white with pink highlights and gilded.
Period 1st and 2nd period.

BLARNEY

Modelled by Fredrick Slater, probably named after Castle Blarney. To this day people flock to 'kiss' the Blarney stone hoping for the gift of speech!
Colour Ways: White, light pink trim.
Period 2nd.

CELTIC

Madam Boroniuxz, a Hungarian, worked at the pottery under E'Loyd 1920–1926. Referring to the books of Kells, she adapted the illustrations to form these Celtic patterns. Four shapes were used for decoration – Ring-handle blanks and three new designs called Low, Tall Celtic and the Three Leg pot. All four are quite different.

CELTIC RING-HANDLE 'CELTIC LOW'
CELTIC HIGH
CELTIC, THREE LEG TEA SET

To-date unrecorded.

CHINESE TEA WARE

Belleek exhibited this set at the Dublin Exhibition in 1872 the Pottery's first major exhibition. A very different design to their normal range but not practical – the tea would be cold before reaching the lips.
Colour Ways: White, white and gilded and exceptional colours.
Periods 1 period, re-introduced 1991 as collectors piece.

CONE

A fir pattern is impressed on the tray and the finial on the teapot represents small fir cones.
Colour Range: Plain, or green, pink, and butterscotch.
Period 2nd period.

ECHINUS

Pronounced (E-k-inus). The name is derived from the Greek *ekhinos* meaning – hedgehog skinned. Echinus Demotter is the proper name for the Sea Urchin upon which this design by Mrs Annie Langley Nairn (FRS) is based. The real sea creature has five radii. Belleek's derivation sometimes has six. Queen Victoria ordered one of these tea sets for herself and another to give as a present to the Empress of Germany.
Colour Ways: Plain white, white with gold trim, pink trim, green trim, and bright orange tinge.
Periods 1st, 2nd.

ERNE

Named after the lake and the river Erne upon which the pottery is situated.
Colour Ways: White, white and cob, green tinge, and pink tinge.
Period 2nd period only.

FAN

Colour Ways: White, white and cob, decorated.
Periods 1st and 2nd period.

FINNER WARE

Named after one of the Townlands in which the Town of
Belleek lies. Finner translated from Gaelic means 'Fair Plain'.
Period 2nd.

FIVE O'CLOCK TEA SET

Designed by Harris. The handle is shaped as 5 o'clock.
Colour Ways: Green, white and cob.
Period 2nd.

GRASS

One of Belleek's most popular sets. When building up sets care
must be taken to match the colours as they vary considerably.
Mainly found in first period, but also found in most other
periods.

HEXAGON

The plain shape of this set lends itself to the artists brush so
Hexagon blanks were often used for the painted sets.
Colour Ways: Colour tints to be found: gold, green, pink, cob
and butterscotch.
Period 2nd period.

INSTITUTE WARE

Through Kerr of Chapel Street, Dublin, Queen Victoria ordered
a breakfast service. Kerr commissioned the design from Miss
Kealy of the Queen's Institute of Female Professional Schools,
Dublin. She was one of the 'gentlewomen of limited means'
trained by this charitable institute for jobs in industry, the Post
Office or professions. The design was registered at the Patent
Office on 12 November, 1870. Unlike other named tea sets
'Institute' pattern on the plates is different on the plates to that
on the cups and saucers.
Colour Ways: White on cob, pink and turquoise.
Periods 1st and 2nd period.

IVY

Colour Ways: Ivy leaves highlighted with (early pink) cob or
green.
Periods 1st period and 3rd period.

LACE

A very decorative pattern lending itself to many combinations
of decoration. Fredrick Slater re-designed this set in the 1900's.
Colour Ways: White, white and cob, white and gold.
Periods 1st and 2nd. Earlier pieces are footed.

HIGH LILY

Not to be confused with Low Lily which is totally different but
as the pieces are scarce it can be difficult to familiarise oneself
with the patterns.
Colour Ways: Green
Period 2nd period.

LIMPET

A very popular design based upon the sea limpet and which was
produced during most periods. The pieces were footed in earlier
sets but Frederick Slater re-modelled the design in the early
1900's.
Periods Most periods.

MASK

The chubby, laughing face seen in this design represents
Bacchus, the noisy and riotus god of wine; hence the vine leaves
and grapes incorporated into the rest of the design.
Colour Ways: White and white with cob, green and pink.
Period 3rd period and later.

NEPTUNE

This design is named after Neptune was Lord of the Seas, aptly
so as it incorporates several sea shells. Figured are the Common
Limpet, and the Blue Rayed Limpet and the Scallop with Coral
for a handle and Small Pond Snail shells for feet.
Colour Ways: White, cob, green, pink, butterscotch and
coloured.
Periods 2nd and all other periods.

RING-HANDLE

A most popular blank, the simple design leaving the ware ready
for different decorations. Other potteries also used the Ring-
Handle shape.
Period 1st period.

THE LIMOGES DECORATION

Introduced by Armstrong, at the time this was a new form of decoration. The picture is built up with a clay mixture and then painted with enamel. Found in First Period. Two most common patterns – THE STORK and CONVOLVULUS.

SCROLL

Colour Ways: Green, pink.
Period 2nd period.

SHELL

Designed using a mixture of shells and coral. Like the Limpet service the earlier pieces were footed, but re-modelled by Frederick Salter.
Colour Ways: White, pink, pink and gold.
Periods 1st and other periods.

SYDNEY

Colour Ways: Green, pink.
Period 2nd period.

THISTLE

Colour Ways: White, pink trim
Period 1st period and reintroduced in gold

THORN

The Thorn pattern is based on a branch of the Hawthorn in blossom combined with a spider's web. Registered at the Patent office on 27 April, 1878 giving Belleek copyright for three years.
Colour Ways: Pink, orange, turquoise, brown, black.
Period 1st.

TRIDACNA

Tridacna is the Latin name for a group of Clam Shells found in Tropical pacific Ocean. They grow to a huge size and are fluted with ribs for strength.
Colour Ways: White, pink, green, blue
Periods Most periods.

VICTORIA

Colour Ways: White, pink, green.
Period 2nd period.

PATTERN X

This pattern is unrecorded, but seemed to have been used to a large extent during the early days.

Part I – Pottery Management History

Part II – Names

D McBirney & Co

1857 – 84	Robert Williams Armstrong

Belleek Pottery Works Co Ltd

1884 – 84	Joshua Poole
1884 – 1900	James Cleary
1900 – 19	Edward Cleary

Belleek Pottery Limited

1920 – 22	Mr Derrigan
1922 – 25	Mr K. E. Leod
1925 – 30	Mr J. F. Dolan
1930 – 31	Mr Michael Dolan
1931 – 33	Mr Upton
1933 – 40	Harry Arnold
1940 – 66	Eric Arnold
1966 – 67	Cyril Arnold

	MANAGING DIRECTOR	GENERAL MANAGER
1967 – 78	Patrick O'Neil	Tommy Campbell
1978 – 82	Shaun O'Loughlin	

Industrial Development Board Control

1982 – 84	Roger Troughton	Jim Barclay

Acquired by Roger Troughton

1984 – 88	Roger Troughton	Jim Barclay

Acquired by Powerscreen International plc

	MANAGING DIRECTOR	PRODUCTION DIRECTOR
1988 – 90	Barry Crosgrove	Arthur Goan

Acquired by George Moore

1990 – 91	Barry Crosgrove	Arthur Goan
1991 –	John Maguire	Arthur Goan

ABERDEEN, James Campbell Hamilton Gordon, 7th Earl & Marquis of Aberdeen, Viceroy of Ireland 1886. His wife, Lady Aberdeen, was a promoter of the arts and also much involved in the issue of women's health. Lectured all over Ireland including Belleek.

ALLINGHAM, LOUISE and MAUDE. Daughters of William Allingham (half-brother of the poet Allingham). They lived in Ballyshannon, only four miles from the Pottery, and earned a little money painting on porcelain which they would bring to the Pottery to be fired. They also painted on Belleek blanks. Their work was mostly signed.

AMPHORA. Greek or Roman vessel with handles on both sides at the neck and pointed at the bottom to spike in the ground. Design source of the 'Amphora' centrepieces and lamps.

ARMSTRONG, ANNIE (1828–88). The daughter of George Nairn. She was a landscape painter and designer exhibiting at the Royal Hibernian Academy from 1844 to 1847. About 1848 she married R. W. ARMSTRONG. She worked very closely with Gallimore when he came from Goss, so it is difficult to attribute work to either but the Artichoke Tea Ware is thought to have been her design.

ARMSTRONG, KATIE. Daughter of William Armstrong. She was responsible for the design of the Neptune Tea Ware.

ARMSTRONG, WILLIAM. S. Co-founder of the pottery.

ARNOLD, CYRIL. Eric's brother. Head of the decorating department from 1946 to 1966. Took over the management after Eric Arnold's sudden death in 1966.

ARNOLD, ERIC. Harry's brother, Managing Director 1940–66. In 1946 he installed two biscuit kilns designed by Allport of Stoke.

ARNOLD, HARRY. Manager 1933–40.

BACCHUS. God of wine, featured on 'Mask' ware.

BLACK. Reputed to have been one of the men who came with W. Bromley from Goss.

BLARNEY. Blarney Castle. People flock to kiss the Blarney stone which will give them the gift of flattering speech!

BOOK OF KELLS. A beautifully illustrated manuscript containing the four Gospels and generally dated c. A.D 800.

BORONIUXZ, MADAME. A Hungarian designer who worked for the Pottery from 1922 to 1926, during K.E. Leod's management. She introduced the Celtic range from designs adapted from the Book of Kells. Modelled by F. Slater.

BOWLER. Head kiln man. Returned to England in the 80's.

BROMLEY, WILLIAM. Foreman at Goss, Stoke-on-Trent.

He joined Belleek in 1863, bringing with him William Gallimore, Goss's chief modeller, and some eleven other craftsmen. He returned to Goss in 1868. Then in 1883 he emigrated to the USA to manage OTT & Brewer.
BURDON. Came with W. Bromley.

CAVALIER. Supporter of King Charles in the Civil War of 1640–60.
CLEARY, EDWARD. Manager 1900–19. A painter before taking over from his brother as manager.
CLEARY, FERGUS. Grandson of James Cleary, he came to the pottery in 1978 and worked in the modelling department. Responsible for several new designs.
CLEARY, JAMES. Manager 1884–1900. Designed and modelled the Cleary range. Trained by Gallimore and succeeded him as Head of the Modelling Department. During his management, Belleek won a Gold Medal at the 1887 Adelaide Exhibition in Australia. His indenture is still in existence, showing his starting pay to be 2s. 6d. a week.
CLYTIE. A water nymph who fell in love with Apollo. Her love was unrequited and she was transformed into a sunflower.

DERRIGAN. Manager 1920–22.
DICKENS, CHARLES (1812–1870). A popular bust produced by a number of potteries.
DOLAN, FRANCIS JOSEPH. Manager 1925–30. A native of Belleek and mainly noted for his success in increasing pottery sales abroad.
DOLAN, MICHAEL. Manager 1930–31. He was a genius with applied flower work on baskets, mirrors and frames and responsible for the introduction of large covered baskets. He left Belleek in 1926 to work for Crown Derby, returning to Ireland in 1938. He died in 1951.
DUNBAR, REVD HALAHAN. Curate at Belleek from 1865 to 1867. An amateur modeller, he is reputed to have modelled the Group of Hounds.

ELLIS, J. Coming from Stoke, he was considered to be one of the Pottery's most skilled painters and is best known for 'The Shoeing of the Bay Mare'.

FINNER. Gaelic translation 'Wood of the Ford'. The second Townland within which Belleek lies.

GALLAGHER, HUGH. Trained by Slater and worked in the modelling department. Retired in 1982.
GALLIMORE, WILLIAM WOOD. Among the most important craftsmen Armstrong enticed from England. Gallimore studied at Art School in Stoke-on-Trent before entering the studio of George Read (a well-known modeller). Later he studied figure modelling under Louis Kremer. Before arriving in Belleek in 1863 as Chief Modeller, Gallimore had been employed in several of the English potteries including Copeland and Goss. Through these factories he would have had experience with parian. It is difficult to attribute actual designs to Gallimore, as his work overlapped with that of Mrs Armstrong, but between them they produced

over five hundred designs. He is known to have modelled the bust of Charles Dickens. In the early 1880s, after losing his right arm in a shooting accident, he returned to Goss and continued his work there. Eventually he emigrated to America as designer for a number of potteries. He died in 1891.
GAVIGAN, JOE Trained in the modelling department with Gallagher, under Slater.

HARRIS, A Painter, modeller and transfer artist, he left Belleek in 1910. Best known for his Five o'Clock Tea Set.
HENSHALL, ALBERT. William Henshall's son, he came to Belleek as a boy with his family. He learned to paint whilst at the pottery, but returned to England in early manhood.
HENSHALL, WILLIAM. Coming from England, Henshall introduced basket making and flower modelling. He also painted on porcelain and a wall plaque of pheasants set in a woodland scene is signed by him. He remained with Belleek until he died in 1902.
HORRIGAN. Came with W. Bromley.

JOHNSTONE, GERTRUDE. Daughter of David Johnstone, a Belleek hotelier, she was a gifted artist who painted the most beautiful flowers on Belleek blanks, but worked outside the Pottery. Unlike Sheerin she rarely signed her work. She died in 1902 whilst still in her late twenties.
KIRK, W. BOYTON. Son of a Dublin sculptor, he worked for Royal Worcester where he modelled many of Royal Worcester's parian figures. He had a close association with Belleek, advising Armstrong on the development of parian and is thought to have modelled the 'Belgian Hawkers'. He was also responsible for modelling the famous Shakespeare service made from Fermanagh clay which won the Gold Award at the Dublin exhibition in 1853.

LEINSTER. One of the four provinces of Ireland and known as the province of the farmers. Throughout the early centuries of Irish history the people of Leinster were obliged to render the High King of Ireland a tribute, known as the 'borama' (cow counting).
LENNOX. Came with W. Bromley.
LEOD, K. E. Manager 1922–25. Responsible for the revival of porcelain and the reduction of earthenware. He modernised the works and increased trade with America.
LIPTON, SIR THOMAS. Scottish grocer, self-made man and millionaire. He realised the potential of supplying the public with groceries and is said to have painted his name on a herd of pigs which he then let loose on the streets of Glasgow, causing havoc but ensuring that no-one forgot his name. He was on his way to Australia when he stopped in Ceylon and there became interested in the potential of 'Tea Gardens', many of which he bought, thus entering the tea trade. He is also well known for competing in the America's Cup which he did five times, and as a supporter of the arts.

MAGUIRE, MICHAEL. A pupil of Gallimore he was

responsible for designing the Shamrock ware which was modelled by Gallimore. Shamrock ware has stood the test of time and is still in production today.

McDERMOTT, THOMAS. A local man who worked as a painter and gilder for Belleek about 1878.

McFERRAN. A parian caster who came with W. Bromley.

McGARRIGLE, MICHAEL. A local man who worked as a painter and gilder for Belleek about 1868.

McKINLEY, WILLIAM (1843–1901). 25th President of the USA whose protectionist tariffs necessitated the first Belleek mark change.

MOOHAN, PATRICK. A local man who worked as a painter and gilder with McGarrigle in 1868.

MOOR. Family living at Cliff House near Belleek.

PATTERSON. Came with W. Bromley.

POOLE, JOSHUA. The first manager of the Belleek Pottery Works Co. Ltd., formed after Armstrong's death in 1884. Highly recommended but remained only a few months before leaving and emigrating to East Liverpool, Ohio. There he managed the art section of Knowles, Taylor and Knowles, one of the American potteries to name their products 'Belleek'.

POPE. Came with W. Bromley.

RANKIN. Came with W. Bromley.

RATHMORE. Gaelic translation 'Big Fort'. North-east of Belleek is the Townland of Rathmore which takes its name from the early fort, dating back to AD 800–900, which used to overlook the village.

ROYALS. Carpenter who came with W. Bromley.

ROUNDHEAD. Supporter of Oliver Cromwell and Parliament in the Civil War, 1640–60.

RYLES, ROBERT. Recorded as working at the pottery in 1874.

SCARLET, SAM. Head mould-maker from Stoke. Drowned in the Erne in 1880s.

SHAMROCK. National emblem of Ireland. Legend tells us that St Patrick, whilst trying to explain the Holy Trinity to the Chiefs of Ireland on the Hill of Tara, used a shamrock to illustrate the 'three in one'.

SHEERIN, EUGENE (1856–1915). From Trillick in County Tyrone. Eugene developed rheumatic fever at the age of four, leaving him an invalid and confined to a wheelchair. At an exhibition in Belfast in 1887 Armstrong noticed Eugene's work and offered him a job in Belleek's decorating department. He lived in No. 1 Rathmore Terrace – which used to be known as English Row, having been built to house the 'skilled English' workers brought to Belleek by Armstrong to train the Irish. Sherrin trained under J. Ellis, the famous painter, and attended the Dublin School of Art. His principal and most beautiful work was a breakfast service commissioned by Dr O. Ternan: fifty-eight pieces, each painted with a different named view of Ireland. When Sherrin's nephew, who cared for him at Belleek, died, Sherrin retired to Dublin and lived with his brother.

SLATER, FREDERICK. Came to Belleek from England in 1893. He married a local girl and remained in Belleek. He was responsible for the International Centre Piece, the largest piece ever made by Belleek. This took six weeks to create and won a gold medal at the Paris Exhibition in 1900. Slater modelled the Blarney, and re-modelled the New Shell and the Limpet tea sets. He died in 1931.

SYDENHAM, JAMES (1624–89). English doctor of world repute.

TARA. Hill of Tara, County Meath. The coronation place of Kings of Ireland. Abandoned in the sixth century AD.

THORNHILL, GEORGE. A local man who worked as a painter and gilder for Belleek around 1874.

TROUGHTON, ROGER. He was initially appointed MD of Belleek Pottery Limited by the IDB but after two years made an offer to buy the Pottery, which was accepted. His offer left him owning 70% of the Company, with the other 30% owned by Allied Irish Bank.

UPTON. Manager 1931–33. Known as 'the earthenware man'. Dedicated to earthenware, Mr Upton organised a sale to dispose of excess parian stock. Trestle tables were erected outside the Pottery and parian pieces were displayed. Times were hard and most of the sales made were for 2d. and 3d. per piece. After three days the sale was brought to an end and Mr Upton ordered workmen to go out and use sledge-hammers to break up any remaining pieces. Unfortunately these were the larger pieces which are now so rare.

VENUS. Roman Goddess of Beauty, Growth and Love, identified with the Greek Aphrodite – Goddess of Love.

WALKINS. Came with W. Bromley.

WESLEY, JOHN (1703–91). Founder of the Methodist Church. He also preached at Belleek.

Belleek Pottery Catalogue, 1904

T HE following pages, containing reproductions of the pieces illustrated in the 1904 Belleek Pottery Catalogue, have been photographed from a rare copy in the Enniskillen Public Library, County Fermanagh.

[Above]
MINSTREL COMPORT (DS.19), MINSTREL CENTRE PIECE (CP.10), BITTERN COMPORT (DS.5)

[Left]
Left to right, first row LILY JUG TALL (JU.57), ULSTER VASE (VS.242), TULIP VASE TRIPLE (VS.238), TULIP CENTRE PIECE (CP.20), TYPHER JUG (JU.86).
Second row MARINE VASE, small (VS.160), IMPERIAL CENTREPIECE (CP.6), HIPPIRITUS CENTREPIECE (CP.5)

[Opposite, top]

First row FIGURE OF BATHER *(ST.2)*, BOY WITH FISH SPILL
(VS.22), SINGLE BOY AND SHELL *(VS.18)*, MINSTREL PAPER
WEIGHT *(MI.67)*, DOUBLE BOY AND SHELL *(VS.20)*, GROUP
OF GREYHOUNDS *(ST.13)*, VENUS AND SHELL *(ST.32)*,
CLYTIE *(ST.8)*, BELGIAN HAWKER FEMALE *(MI.37)*
Second row CROUCHING VENUS *(ST.9)*, AFFECTION *(ST.1)*,
BASKET CARRIER GIRL *(MI.36)*, JACK ON SHORE BOX
(MI.16), PRISONER OF LOVE *(ST.9)*, BASKET CARRIER BOY
(MI.35), JACK AT SEA BOX *(MI.15)*, MEDITATION *(ST.25)*,
BELGIAN HAWKER MALE *(MI.38)*, CAVALIER *(ST.4)*

[Opposite, bottom]

First row FINNER JARDINIÈRE *(FP.24)*, BELLEEK
JARDINIÈRE UNFOOTED *(FP.4)*, THORN JARDINIÈRE
(FP.53), RATHMORE JARDINIÈRE UNFOOTED *(FP.47)*,
FLOWER POT FOOTED, small *(FP.26)*, FLOWER POT FOOTED,
large *(FP.25)*
Second row BELLEEK FLOWER POT, small *(FP.6)*, PIERCED
SPILL *(VS.176)*, BELLEEK POT FLOWERED, middle *(FP.5)*
Third row OAK JARDINIÈRE *(FP.34)*, BELLEEK JARDINIÈRE
FOOTED *(FP.3)*, PANEL JARDINIÈRE FOOTED *(FP.40)*,
RATHMORE JARDINIÈRE FOOTED *(FP.46)*, LIPTON
JARDINIÈRE FOOTED *(FP.30)*

[Above]

First row FRUIT BASKET *(DS.12)*, DOLPHIN AND SHELL
DESSERT PLATE *(DS.10)*, DOLPHIN AND SHELL COMPORT
(DS.8), GREEK COMPORT *(DS.16)*, GREEK DESSERT PLATE
(DS.17)
Second row BOY BOMBINEER COMPORT *(DS.7)*, THORN PLATE
(DS.22), THORN COMPORT *(DS.21)*
Third row BASKET COMPORT LOW *(DS.2)*, VINE COMPORT
(DS.35), BASKET DESSERT PLATE *(DS.4)*, BOY SWAN
COMPORT *(DS.6)*, PRINCE OF WALES COMPORT *(CP.11)*,
TRIHORSE COMPORT *(DS.33)*, VINE DESSERT PLATE *(DS.37)*

[Above]

First row DIANA VASE PIERCED *(VS.68)*, DIAMOND JUG
PIERCED *(JU.32)*, ABERDEEN JUGS UNFLOWERED, large,
medium, small *(JU.4,5,6)*, PRINCE ARTHUR VASE
UNFLOWERED *(VS.3)*, MASK JUG FOOTED *(JU.60)*
Second row ELCHO VASE *(VS.85)*, TRIPLE DOLPHIN AND
WINKLE *(VS.74)*, IRISH HARP, small *(MI.45)*, STRAW BASKET
(MI.4), IRISH HARP, large *(MI.44)*, ERNE BASKET *(MI.1)*,
DIANA VASE *(VS.67)*
Third row TULIP VASE, single *(VS.235)*, NILE VASE, medium,
large, small *(VS.169/8/170)*, MOOR VASE *(VS.163)*, ISLAND
VASE *(VS.146)*, SHELL SPILL TRIPLE *(VS.214)*

[Opposite]

First row BIRD VASE PAINTED *(VS.15)*, ABERDEEN
FLOWERED, large *(JU.1)*, TABLE CENTREPIECE *(CP.18)*
Second row BIRD TREE STUMP VASE *(VS.12)*, ABERDEEN
FLOWERED, medium *(JU.2)*, ABERDEEN FLOWERED, small
(JU.3)
Third row PRINCESS VASE FLOWERED *(VS.178)*
Fourth row HENSHALL SPILL, flowered *(VS.126)*
Fifth row FLOWERED FRAME, small and large *(FR.6/5)*, THISTLE
VASE *(VS.226)*
Sixth row SHELL AND CORAL FRAME, medium *(FR.12)*,
DOUBLE PHOTO FRAME *(FR.3)*, FLOWERED FRAME, middle
(FR.4)

[Above]

First row SHAMROCK JARDINIÈRE *(FP.50)*, NAIADS
JARDINIÈRE TALL *(FP.32)*, FERN JARDINIÈRE, large *(FP.20)*
Second row PIERCED FLOWER POT, small *(FP.43)*, NAIADS
JARDINIÈRE *(FP.31)*, FERN JARDINIÈRE, medium/small
(FP.21,22), PIERCED FLOWER POT, large *(FP.42)*

[Above]

First row BELLEEK FLOWER TROUGH (FP.12), VICTORIA BASKET (VS.254), LEINSTER VASE (VS.152), VICTORIA SHELL (VS.255), SEAHORSE AND SHELL (VS.205), SEAHORSE FLOWER HOLDER (VS.206), NAUTILUS ON CORAL (VS.164)

Second row ERNE COVERED VASE (VS.89), CORAL AND SHELL VASE (VS.60), MARINE JUG (JU.59), MARINE VASE, large (VS.159), VICTORIA VASE (VS.256), DOLPHIN AND SHELL (VS.75)

Third row IMPERIAL SHELL (VS.132), FERMANAGH VASE (VS.94), CLAM SHELL AND GRIFFIN (VS.48), CLAM SHELL (VS.50), HONEYSUCKLE VASE (VS.130), TRIPLE CORAL AND SHELL (VS.61)

[Above]

First row SYDENHAM TWIG, small (BS.77), SHAMROCK BASKET, small (BS.71), SYDENHAM TWIG, large (BS.75), SHAMROCK BASKET, large (BS.70), SYDENHAM, middle (BS.76)

Second row FORGET ME NOT TRINKET BOX (MI.19), SHAMROCK TRINKET BOX (MI.21)

Third row OVAL COVERED, large (BS.42), FLOWERED BOWL (VS.106), RATHMORE BASKET (BS.54)

Fourth row OVAL COVERED, small (BS.43), ROUND NO.8 (BS.41), HENSHALL'S TWIG, large (BS.25), OVAL BASKET, large (BS.44)

Fifth row HENSHALL'S TWIG, small (BS.29), BIRD'S NEST BASKET (BS.1), CONVOLVULUS (BS.14), OVAL BASKET, small (BS.52), ROUND COVERED BASKET (BS.61)

[Opposite bottom]

First row TRIPLE SPILL, large and small (VS.233/4), SINGLE HIPPIRITUS (VS.128), IVY TREE STUMP SPILL (VS.148), AMPHORA, large, medium, small (CP.1/2/3), SINGLE ROOT SPILL (VS.197), QUIVER VASE (VS.180), IVY TRUNK STUMP VASE (VS.149)

Second row FEATHER VASE, large and small (VS.92/3), ONION SPILL, large and small (VS.171/2), PANEL VASE, large and small (VS.174/5), HAND HOLDING FAN (VS.122), ROCK SPILL, small, medium, large (VS.196/5/4), SCALE VASE (VS.204)

Third row CANE SPILL, large, medium, small (VS.8/9/10), FLYING FISH VASE (VS.112), DOUBLE RIBBON SPILL (VS.185), DOUBLE ROCK SPILL (VS.192), CACTUS SPILL (VS.28), TRIPLE FLOWER HOLDER (VS.104)

[Above]

First row PRINCESS VASE *(VS.179)*, LILY BASKET *(MI.3)*, FINNER JUG *(JU.39)*, TOBACCO BREWER *(MI.58)*, RIBBON VASE *(VS.186)*, DAISY VASE *(VS.65)*, FLAT FISH VASE *(VS.102)*

Second row HAREBELL VASE *(VS.124)*, FROG VASE, large *(VS.115)*, BRANCH CANE SPILL *(VS.32)*, FISH ON TAIL *(VS.96)*, SPECIMEN HOLDER, large and small *(VS.219/220)*, LIMPET VASE *(VS.157)*, SUNFLOWER VASE *(VS.222)*, DOLPHIN SPILL *(VS.77)*

Third row INDIAN CORN SPILL *(VS.136)*, SHAMROCK SPILL (ONION) *(SHA.87)*, SHAMROCK SPILL (CONE) *(SHA.85)*, CLEARY SPILL, large and small *(VS.52/3)*, LILY SPILL, small *(VS.155)*, SNAKE SPILL *(VS.218)*, THISTLE TOP *(VS.225)*, FLUTED SPILL, small and medium *(VS.111/110)*, TYPHER SPILL *(VS.240)*, CORN FLOWER SPILL *(VS.62)*, RIBBON SPILL *(VS.184)*, LILY SPILL, large *(VS.154)*

[Above left]

First row IRISH POT, size 5–1 *(VS.140/5)*, NICKEL FLOWER POT *(FP.33)*

Second row TOY FERN *(FP.23)*, BELLEEK FLOWER POT, tiny *(FP.7)*, CRINKLED FLOWER POT *(FP.17)*, IRISH POT *(VS.142)*, GRASS MUG *(TGR.13)*, ROPE HANDLE MUG *(TM.40)*, SHAMROCK MUG, small *(SHA.13)*, THORN MUG, small *(TTO.13)*, CLEARY MUG *(TM.38)*

Third row OCTAGONAL FLOWER POT, medium and small *(FP.35/6)*, BELLEEK FLOWER POT, medium and small *(FP.10/11)*, CONE VASE, medium and small *(VS.58/9)*, DIAMOND FLOWER POT *(FP.18)*

Fourth row DOUBLE SHELL *(VS.82)*, CONCH SHELL VASE *(VS.245)*, CRINKLED FLOWER POT *(FP.16)*, BOAT ASH TRAY *(TM.1)*, PIG, small and large *(MI.54/53)*

[Above]

First row IRISH POT AND CREAM, large and small (*TM.24/3*), SHAMROCK SUGAR AND CREAM (*SHA.55*), LILY SUGAR AND CREAM (*JU.56*), RATHMORE CREAM (*JU.66*)

Second row IVY SUGAR, large (*TIV.20*), IVY JUG, large (*TIV.19*), IVY SUGAR, medium (*TIV.21*), IVY JUG, small (*TIV.17*), IVY SUGAR AND CREAM, small (*TIV.22/17*), LILY SCROLL SUGAR AND CREAM (*JU.55*)

Third row RIBBON CREAM AND SUGAR (*JU.68*), LOTUS CREAM AND SUGAR (*JU.58*), TRIDACNA BOAT SUGAR AND CREAM (*TTR.47*), FAN MINIATURE SUGAR AND CREAM (*JU.38*), CLEARY SUGAR AND CREAM (*JU.28*).

Fourth row TOY SHELL SUGAR AND CREAM (*JU.81*), DAIRY SUGAR AND CREAM (*JU.30*), SHELL SUGAR AND CREAM (*JU.73*), SWAN, large and small (*MI.55/6*).

[Opposite top]

First row CARDIUM SHELL ON CORAL, size 1–4 (*VS.37–40*), CARDIUM ON SHELL, size 1–4 (*VS.33–6*)

Second row FLOWERED BOX CRATE (*MI.13*), TRIPLE CARDIUM ON SHELL WITH CORAL (*VS.41–4*)

Third row APPLELEAF INKSTAND (*MI.27*), FLOWERED JEWEL STAND (*BS.18*), LIMPET SHELL SALT (*TLI.51*), SHAMROCK SALT (*SHA.51*), MERMAID INKSTAND (*MI.28*)

Fourth row APPLELEAF CANDLESTICK (*CL.4*), FLOWERED MENU FLOWER HOLDER (*TM.36*), DRAPERY SCENT BOTTLE (*MI.7*), TRIPLE SHELL TRINKET STAND (*TSH.74*), NAUTILUS ON SHELL (*VS.165*), NAUTILUS JUG (*JU.65*)

[Opposite, bottom]

First row ROUND TUMBLER 1–6 (*TM.70–6*), MOUSTACHE TUMBLER 1/2 (*TM.64/5*), DOUBLE CREAM (*JU.33*)

Second row SALT TUB (*TM.50/1*), HEXAGON SALT (*THE.51*), BOAT SALT (*TM.44*), DIAMOND SALT (*TM.47*), LILY SALT (*THL.51*), SHELL SALT (*TSH.51*), EMERSON MUG (*TM.39*), LIFFORD JUG (*JU.54*), WINE GLASS, large (*TM.77*)

Third row SHAMROCK CRUET (*SHA.53*), UNDINE CREAM (*JU.87*), SCALE JUG (*JU.72*), MUSSEL SPOON (*TM.58*), WORCESTER SALT (*TM.53*), CONCH SHELL VASE (*VS.57*), DAIRY CRUET (*TM.19*)

Fourth row MASK JUG (*JU.61*), TOY SHELL JUG (*JU.81*), WINE GLASS MIDDLE (*TM.78*), FAN TUMBLERS 1–6 (*TFA.57–63*)

[Opposite, top]

All Tridacna

First row SLOP, large *(TTR.25)*, SUGAR, large *(TTR.21)*, CREAM, small *(TTR.15)*, BREAD PLATE *(TTR.26)*

Second row TEAPOT, large *(TTR.2)*, KETTLE, large *(TTR.6)*

Third row CUP AND SAUCER *(TTR.8)*, PLATE 5″ *(TTR.28)*

[Opposite, bottom]

All Shamrock

First row TEAPOT, large *(SHA.2)*, CUP AND SAUCER TALL *(SHA.9)*, BREAD PLATE *(SHA.26)*, COFFEE CUP AND SAUCER *(SHA.10)*, KETTLE, large *(SHA.6)*

Second row BREAKFAST CUP AND SAUCER *(SHA.11)*, SUGAR, large *(SHA.21)*, SIDE PLATE *(SHA.27)*, CREAM, large *(SHA.16)*, MOUSTACHE CUP AND SAUCER *(SHA.12)*

Third row COVERED MUFFIN *(SHA.35)*, EGG CUP *(SHA.48)*

Fourth row SLOP, large *(SHA.25)*, CUP AND SAUCER LOW *(SHA.8)*, SUGAR, small *(SHA.20)*, TEAPOT, medium *(SHA.3)*, TRAY *(SHA.1)*, COMPLETE SET, CREAM, small *(SHA.15)*, MILK JUG *(SHA.17)*

[Above]

First row FAN BRUSH TRAY *(TFA.66)*, NEPTUNE BRUSH TRAY *(TNE.66)*, THORN BRUSH TRAY *(TTO.66)*

Second row FAN PIN TRAY *(TFA.65)*, FAN SCENT BOTTLE *(TFA.68)*, NEPTUNE SCENT BOTTLE *(TNE.68)*, NEPTUNE PIN TRAY *(TNE.65)*, THORN PIN TRAY *(TTO.65)*, THORN SCENT BOTTLE *(TTO.68)*, BOY CARRYING CORNUCOPIA *(VS.17)*, BOY CANDELABRA *(CL.13)*

Third row FAN RING PEG *(TFA.67)*, FAN LIP SALVE *(TFA.69)*, FAN BOX TALL *(TFA.73)*, FAN BOX LOW *(TFA.72)*, NEPTUNE RING PEG *(TNE.67)*, NEPTUNE LIP SALVE *(TNE.69)*, NEPTUNE BOX TALL *(TNE.73)*, NEPTUNE BOX LOW *(TNE.72)*, THORN RING PEG *(TTO.67)*, THORN LIP SALVE *(TTO.69)*, THORN BOX TALL *(TTO.72)*, THORN BOX LOW *(TTO.73)*

Fourth row THORN CANDLESTICK *(TTO.80)*, BOY AND VINE CANDLESTICK *(CL.8)*, NIGHT LIGHT HOLDER *(CL.18)*, PIANO CANDLESTICK *(CL.20)*, ALLINGHAM CANDLESTICK *(CL.1)*, ANCHORITE CANDLESTICK *(CL.3)*, DOLPHIN AND BOY CANDLESTICK *(CL.15)*

[Above]

All Hexagon

First row SLOP, large *(THE.24)*, SUGAR, large *(THE.21)*, CREAM, large *(THE.16)*, BREAD PLATE *(THE.26)*, COVERED MUFFIN *(THE.35)*, SIDE PLATE *(THE.27)*, MILK JUG *(THE.17)*, CUP ON TRAY *(THE.63)*

Second row TEAPOT, large *(THE.4)*, EGG CUP *(THE.48)*, COFFEE CUP *(THE.10)*, KETTLE, large *(THE.5)*

Third row MOUSTACHE CUP AND SAUCER *(THE.12)*, SUGAR, small *(THE.20)*, TRAY *(THE.1)*, TEAPOT, medium *(THE.3)*, CREAM, small *(THE.15)*, CUP AND SAUCER *(THE.8)*, COMPLETE SET, BREAKFAST CUP AND SAUCER *(THE.11)*

[Above]

All Echinus

First row CREAM, large *(TEC.16)*, SUGAR, large *(TEC.21)*, SLOP *(TEC.24)*

Second row BREAD PLATE *(TEC.26)*. KETTLE, large *(TEC.5)*, TEAPOT, large *(TEC.2)*

Third row CUPS AND SAUCERS *(TEC.8)*, SIDE PLATE *(TEC.27)*.

[Opposite, top]

All Neptune

First row TEAPOT, large *(TNE.2)*, BREAD PLATE *(TNE.26)*, KETTLE, large *(TNE.5)*

Second row SLOP, large *(TNE.24)*, COFFEE CUP AND SAUCER *(TNE.10)*, SIDE PLATE *(TNE.27)*

Third row SUGAR, large *(TNE.22)*, SUGAR, small *(TNE.20)*, TRAY *(TNE.1)*, TEAPOT, medium *(TNE.3)*, CUP AND SAUCER *(TNE.8)*, CREAM, small *(TNE.15)*, COMPLETE SET, CREAM, large *(TNE.16)*

[Opposite bottom]

First row ERNE KETTLE *(TER.5)*, CONE CUP AND SAUCER *(TCO.8)*, CONE TEAPOT *(TCO.3)*, CONE CREAM, small *(TCO.15)*, CONE TRAY *(TCO.1)*, CONE SUGAR, small *(TCO.20)*, CONE COMPLETE SET, CONE KETTLE *(TCO.5)*

Second row ERNE BREAD PLATE *(TER.26)*, ERNE SIDE PLATE *(TER.27)*, CONE SLOP, large *(TCO.24)*, CONE SUGAR, large *(TCO.21)*, CONE SIDE PLATE *(TCO.27)*, CONE BREAD PLATE *(TCO.26)*

Third row CONE CREAM, large *(TCO.16)*, ERNE SUGAR *(TER.20)*, ERNE TRAY *(TER.1)*, ERNE TEAPOT *(TER.3)*, ERNE CUP AND SAUCER *(TER.8)*, ERNE COMPLETE SET, ERNE CREAM *(TER.15)*, CONE SLOP *(TCO.24)*, CONE COFFEE CUP AND SAUCER *(TCO.10)*

[Opposite, top]

All Tridacna

First row KETTLE, large *(TTR.6)*, COVERED MUFFIN DISH
(TTR.35), BREAD PLATE *(TTR.26)*, TEAPOT, large *(TTR.2)*,
PLATE 5″ *(TTR.28)*

Second row MOUSTACHE CUP AND SAUCER *(TTR.12)*, EGG CUP
(TTR.48), COFFEE CUP AND SAUCER *(TTR.10)*, BREAKFAST
CUP AND SAUCER *(TTR.11)*

Third row SLOP, large *(TTR.25)*, CREAM, large *(TTR.16)*,
COMPLETE SET, TRAY *(TTR.1)*, SUGAR, small *(TTR.20)*,
TEAPOT, medium *(TTR.3)*, CREAM, small *(TTR.15)*, CUP AND
SAUCER *(TTR.8)*, SUGAR, large *(TTR.21)*, MILK JUG *(TTR.17)*

[Opposite, bottom]

First row BAMBOO TEAPOT, small *(TM.62)*, SCROLL BREAD
PLATE *(TSC.26)*, BAMBOO TEAPOT, large *(TM.63)*

Second row HIGH LILY CUP ON TRAY *(THL.63)*, SCROLL
TEAPOT *(TSC.3)*, SCROLL SUGAR, large *(TSC.21)*

Third row SCROLL COFFEE CUP AND SAUCER *(TSC.10)*,
SCROLL CREAM, small *(TSC.15)*, SCROLL SUGAR, small
(TSC.20), SCROLL CUP AND SAUCER *(TSC.8)*, SCROLL TRAY
(TSC.1), SCROLL COMPLETE SET, SCROLL SIDE PLATE
(TSC.27)

Fourth row SCROLL SLOP *(TSC.24)*, SCROLL CREAM, large
(TSC.16)

[Above]

First row FLUTED JAM POT *(TM.26)*, CHINESE TEAPOT, large
(TCH.2), CHINESE CUP AND SAUCER *(TCH.8)*, CHINESE
CREAM *(TCH.15)*, CHINESE COMPLETE SET, CHINESE TRAY
(TCH.1), JAM POT RIBBON *(TM.27)*

Second row SHELL BUTTER COVERED *(TSH.32)*, ACORN BOX
(MI.10), COVERED BUTTER TUB *(TM.12)*, ABERDEEN SUGAR
(TAB.20), ABERDEEN TEAPOT *(TAB.3)*, ABERDEEN CREAM
(TAB.15), ABERDEEN CUP AND SAUCER *(TAB.8)*,
ABERDEEN COMPLETE SET, ABERDEEN TRAY *(TAB.1)*

Third row BUTTER TUB *(TM.11)*, HEART TRINKET BOX
(MI.20).

[Opposite top]

First and second row HEART PLATES (*MI.83/2/I*), SHELL BUTTER
DISH (*TM.10*), LEAF PLATES (*MI.84–9*)

Third row ERNE LEAF PLATE (*MI.76/7/8*), HEXAGON TEAPOT
(*THE.3*), HEXAGON CUP AND SAUCER (*THE.8*), HEXAGON
TRAY (*THE.1*), HEXAGON SUGAR (*THE.20*), HEXAGON
CREAM (*THE.15*), HEXAGON COMPLETE SET, SYCAMORE
LEAF PLATE (*MI.106/7/8/9*)

[Opposite, bottom]

First row SHELL BISCUIT JAR (*TSH.39*), SHELL TRAY (*TSH.1*),
SHELL SUGAR, small (*TSH.20*), SHELL TEAPOT (*TSH.3*),
CRATE MATCH BOX (*MI.14*), SHELL CUP AND SAUCER
(*TSH.8*), SHELL CREAM (*TSH.15*), SHELL COMPLETE SET,
DIAMOND BISCUIT JAR (*TM.4*)

Second row SHELL JUG (*JU.74*), SHAMROCK BOX, oval (*SHA.76*),
SHELL SUGAR, large (*TM.59*)

Third row VICTORIA SUGAR (*TVI.20*), SHAMROCK ROUND
BOX (*SHA.77*), VICTORIA COMPLETE SET, VICTORIA TRAY
(*TVI.1*), VICTORIA TEAPOT (*TVI.3*), VICTORIA CUP AND
SAUCER (*TVI.8*), VICTORIA CREAM (*TVI.15*), SHELL
TRINKET BOX (*TSH.72*)

[Above]

First row SHAMROCK HONEY POT ON THREE FEET (*SHA.36*),
LOW LILY SUGAR (*TLL.20*), LOW LILY TEAPOT (*TLL.3*), LOW
LILY CREAM (*TLL.15*), LOW LILY CUP AND SAUCER (*TLL.8*),
LOW LILY COMPLETE SET, LOW LILY TRAY (*TLL.1*),
SARDINE BOX AND STAND (*TM.55*)

Second row MENU HOLDER (*TM.35*), TRIPLE MENU HOLDER
(*TSH.56*)

Third row RATHMORE BISCUIT JAR (*TM.5*), HARP SHAMROCK
SUGAR (*SHP.20*), HARP SHAMROCK TRAY (*SHP.1*), HARP
SHAMROCK TEAPOT (*SHP.3*), HARP SHAMROCK CUP AND
SAUCER (*SHP.8*), HARP SHAMROCK CREAM (*SHP.15*), HARP
SHAMROCK COMPLETE SET, SHAMROCK BISCUIT BARREL
(*SHA.39*)

[Opposite, top]

All High Lily

First row KETTLE (*THL.5*), BREAD PLATE (*THL.26*), SIDE PLATE (*THL.27*)

Second row SUGAR, large (*THL.21*), SUGAR, small (*THL.20*), SLOP (*THL.24*)

Third row CREAM, large (*THL.16*), COMPLETE SET, CREAM, small (*THL.15*), TEAPOT (*THL.3*), TRAY (*THL.1*), CUP AND SAUCER (*THL.8*), COFFEE CUP AND SAUCER (*THL.10*)

[Opposite, bottom]

First row SYDNEY CREAM, large (*TSY.16*), CHURN CRUET (*TM.18*), SHELL CRUET (*TSH.54*), SYDNEY SLOP (*TSY.24*)

Second row SYDNEY BREAD PLATE (*TSY.26*), SHAMROCK EGG FRAME AND CUPS (*SHA.47*), SYDNEY SUGAR, large (*TSY.21*), HIGH LILY CRUET (*THL.54*)

Third row SYDNEY SIDE PLATE (*TSY.27*), SYDNEY CREAM (*TSY.15*), SYDNEY TRAY (*TSY.1*), SYDNEY COMPLETE SET, SYDNEY TEAPOT (*TSY.3*), SYDNEY CUP AND SAUCER (*TSY.8*), SYDNEY SUGAR, small (*TSY.20*)

[Above]

First row HARP HANDLE JUGS (*JU.49/50/1*)), SLATER SWEET (*TM.56*)

Second row BLARNEY COFFEE CUP AND SAUCER (*TBL.10*), M'BIRNEY SWEET (*MI.90*)

Third row BLARNEY SLOP (*TBL.24*), BLARNEY SIDE PLATE (*TBL.27*), BLARNEY TEAPOT (*TBL.3*), BLARNEY BREAD PLATE (*TBL.26*), BLARNEY CREAM, large (*TBL.16*)

Fourth row BLARNEY SWEETMEAT DISH (*TBL.31*), BLARNEY CREAM, small (*TBL.15*), BLARNEY SUGAR, small (*TBL.20*)

Fifth row BLARNEY SUGAR, large (*TBL.21*), BLARNEY COMPLETE SET, BLARNEY TRAY (*TBL.1*), BLARNEY CUP AND SAUCER (*TBL.8*), INSTITUTE HONEY POT (*TIN.36*)

[Above]

All Echinus

First row BREAKFAST CUP AND SAUCER (*TEC.11*), TEAPOT, large (*TEC.2*), MOUSTACHE CUP AND SAUCER (*TEC.12*)

Second row KETTLE, small (*TEC.6*), COVERED MUFFIN DISH (*TEC.35*)

Third row CREAM, large (*TEC.16*), SUGAR SIFTER (*TEC.52*), BREAD PLATE (*TEC.26*), SLOP (*TEC.24*), EGG CUP (*TEC.48*)

Fourth row SUGAR, small (*TEC.20*), TEAPOT, medium (*TEC.3*), SIDE PLATE (*TEC.27*)

Fifth row SUGAR, large (*TEC.21*), COMPLETE SET, TRAY (*TEC.1*), TEA CUP AND SAUCER (*TEC.8*), TEAPOT (*TEC.3*), CREAM (*TEC.15*), COFFEE CUP AND SAUCER (*TEC.10*)

[Opposite, top]

First row BASKET BISCUIT BOX (*TM.2*), FAN BREAD PLATE (*TFA.26*), CRATE BISCUIT BOX (*TM.3*)

Second row FAN SUGAR COVERED, large (*TFA.22*), FAN SLOP (*TFA.24*), SHAMROCK CRUET (*SHA.54*), FAN SIDE PLATE (*TFA.27*)

Third row FAN SUGAR, small (*TFA.20*), FAN TEAPOT (*TFA.3*), FAN CUP AND SAUCER (*TFA.8*), FAN TRAY (*TFA.1*), FAN CREAM, small (*TFA.15*), FAN CREAM, large (*TFA.16*), FAN COFFEE CUP AND SAUCER (*TFA.10*)

[Opposite, bottom]

First row SHELL PLATES (*MI.101/2/3*), OVAL PLATES (*MI.93/4/5/6*)

Second row CUSTARD CUP AND SAUCER (*TM.20*), WORCESTER PLATES (*MI.113/2/1/0*)

Third row FINNER BREAD PLATE (*TFI.26*), FINNER SIDE PLATE (*TFI.27*), FINNER SUGAR, small (*TFI.20*), FINNER TEAPOT (*TFI.3*), FINNER CREAM, small (*TFI.15*), FINNER SLOP, large (*TFI.24*), FINNER COVERED SUGAR (*TFI.21*) FINNER COMPLETE SET, FINNER TRAY (*TFI.1*), FINNER CUP AND SAUCER (*TFI.8*), FINNER CREAM, large (*TFI.16*)

[Above]

First row THORN KETTLE *(TTO.6)*, THORN TEAPOT, large
(TTO.2), THORN JUGS *(JU.78/7/6)*
Second row THORN SIDE PLATE *(TTO.27)*, THORN SUGAR, large
(TTO.21), THORN SLOP *(TTO.24)*, THORN CREAM, large
(TT.16), THORN BREAKFAST CUP AND SAUCER *(TTO.11)*
Third row TRIPLE BUCKET *(VS.24)*, THORN COMPLETE SET,
THORN SUGAR, small *(TTO.20)*, THORN TRAY *(TTO.1)*,
THORN TEAPOT, small *(TTO.4)*, THORN CREAM, small
(TTO.15), THORN CUP AND SAUCER *(TTO.8)*, THORN BREAD
PLATE *(TTO.26)*

[Right]

First row ARTICHOKE BREAD PLATE *(TAR.26)*, ARTICHOKE
EGG CUP *(TAR.48)*, ARTICHOKE SIDE PLATE *(TAR.27)*,
ARTICHOKE SLOP *(TAR.24)*, INSTITUTE BREAKFAST CUP
AND SAUCER *(TIN.11)*, INSTITUTE SLOP *(TIN.24)*,
INSTITUTE 6" PLATE *(TIN.28)*, INSTITUTE EGG CUP
(TIN.48), INSTITUTE BREAD PLATE *(TIN.26)*
Second row ARTICHOKE SUGAR *(TAR.20)*, ARTICHOKE MILK
JUG *(TAR.17)*, INSTITUTE SUGAR COVERED *(TIN.22)*,
INSTITUTE CREAM *(TIN.15)*
Third row ARTICHOKE COVERED MUFFIN DISH *(TAR.35)*,
ARTICHOKE SUGAR COVERED *(TAR.22)*, ARTICHOKE CREAM
(TAR.15), ARTICHOKE TEAPOT *(TAR.3)*, ARTICHOKE TRAY
(TAR.1), ARTICHOKE CUP AND SAUCER *(TAR.8)*,
ARTICHOKE COMPLETE SET, INSTITUTE CUP AND SAUCER
(TIN.8)

[Above]

First row GRASS THREE LEG HONEY *(TGR.36)*, GRASS
KETTLE *(TGR.5)*, GRASS MILK JUG *(TGR.18)*
Second row ERNE LEAF PLATE, large *(MI.76)*, GRASS
MOUSTACHE CUP AND SAUCER *(TGR.12)*
Third row GRASS SLOP *(TGR.24)*, GRASS SUGAR COVERED,
large *(TGR.22)*, GRASS EGG CUP *(TGR.48)*, GRASS CREAM,
large *(TGR.17)*
Fourth row GRASS COVERED MUFFIN DISH *(TGR.35)*, GRASS
CREAM, small *(TGR.15)*, GRASS CUP AND SAUCER *(TGR.8)*,
GRASS TEAPOT, medium *(TGR.3)*, GRASS TRAY *(TGR.1)*,
GRASS SUGAR, small *(TGR.20)*, GRASS COMPLETE SET, GRASS
BREAD PLATE *(TGR.26)*, GRASS SIDE PLATE *(TGR.27)*

[Below, right]

First row SHELL PLATEAU, medium *(MI.115)*, SHELL BISCUIT
BOX, large and small *(TSH.38/9)*, SHELL JELLY OVAL *(TM.30)*
Second row THISTLE CREAM, large *(TTH.16)*, SHELL JELLY
SQUARE *(TM.31)*, THISTLE SIDE PLATE *(TTH.27)*, THISTLE
BREAD PLATE *(TTH.26)*, SHELL PLATEAU, large *(MI.114)*
Third row THISTLE SUGAR, large *(TTH.21)*, THISTLE SLOP
(TTH.24), THISTLE SUGAR, small *(TTH.20)*, THISTLE
COMPLETE SET, THISTLE TRAY *(TTH.1)*, THISTLE TEAPOT
(TTH.3), THISTLE CUP AND SAUCER *(TTH.8)*, THISTLE
CREAM *(TTH.15)*, SHELL JELLY OBLONG *(TM.29)*, SHELL
PLEATEAU, small *(MI.116)*

[Above]
First row ACORN JUG (*JU.8–11*), LACE SLOP (*TLA.24*)
Second row LACE SUGAR, large (*TLA.21*), LACE COFFEE CUP
AND SAUCER (*TLA.10*), FLORENCE JUGS (*JU.43/2/1/40*)
Third row LACE SIDE PLATE (*TLA.27*), LACE SUGAR (*TLA.20*),
LACE TEAPOT (*TLA.3*), LACE CUP AND SAUCER (*TLA.8*),
LACE TRAY (*TLA.1*), LACE CREAM (*TLA.15*), LACE
COMPLETE SET, LACE CREAM, large (*TLA.16*), LACE BREAD
PLATE (*TLA.26*)

[Right]
First row STONEWARE JUGS, LILY STONEWARE JUGS
Second row RING-HANDLE SIDE PLATE (*TRI.27*), RING-
HANDLE COVERED MUFFIN DISH (*TRI.35*), RING-HANDLE
CUP AND SAUCER (*TRI.8*), RING-HANDLE BREAKFAST CUP
AND SAUCER (*TRI.11*)
Third row RING-HANDLE SLOP (*TRI.24*), RING-HANDLE EGG
CUP (*TRI.48*), RING-HANDLE CREAM LOW (*TRI.15*), RING-
HANDLE SUGAR LOW, SMALL (*TRI.20*), TEAPOT (*TRI.3*),
RING-HANDLE TRAY (*TRI.1*), RING-HANDLE COMPLETE
SET, RING-HANDLE CUP AND SAUCER (*TRI.8*), RING-
HANDLE SUGAR LOW, small (*TRI.20*), RING-HANDLE BREAD
PLATE (*TRI.26*), RING-HANDLE COFFEE CUP AND SAUCER
(*TRI.10*)

Belleek Pottery Catalogue, 1949

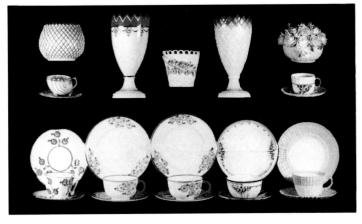

[Above]

First row Unrecorded Cups and Saucers. Part New Shell Tea Set, note the New Shell has no feet. BREAD PLATE (*TNS.26*), PLATE 6″ (*TNS.27*), SUGAR, large (*TNS.21*), CUP AND SAUCER (*TNS.8*), CREAM, large (*TNS.15*).

Second row RING-HANDLE COFFEE POT (*TRI.7*), RING-HANDLE COFFEE CUP AND SAUCER (*TRI.10*), DECORATED NEPTUNE CUP AND SAUCER (*TNE.8*), DECORATED NEPTUNE SIDE PLATE (*TNE.27*)

[Left]

First row DIAMOND FLOWER POT (*FP.18*), NEPTUNE COFFEE CUP AND SAUCER (*TNE.10*), SMOOTH FEATHER VASE (*VS.91*), PIERCED SPILL, flowered (*VS.176*), FEATHER VASE (*VS.92*), ROSE BOWL (*CP.15*), TRIDACNA COFFEE CUP AND SAUCER (*TTR.10*)

Second row These trios all have exceptional decoration. HARP SHAMROCK CUP AND SAUCER (*SHP.8*), HARP SHAMROCK SIDE PLATE (*SHP.27*), THREE TRIDACNA CUPS AND SAUCERS (*TTR.8*), THREE TRIDACNA SIDE PLATES (*TTR.27*)

[Above]

First row HARP SHAMROCK SIDE PLATE *(SHP.27)*, HARP
SHAMROCK BREAD PLATE *(SHP.26)*

Second row SHAMROCK BISCUIT JAR *(SHA.39)*, HARP
SHAMROCK TEAPOT *(SHP.3)*, HARP SHAMROCK COFFEE POT
(SHP.7)

Third row HARP SHAMROCK SLOP *(SHP.24)*, HARP SHAMROCK
SUGAR *(SHP.20)*, HARP SHAMROCK CUP AND SAUCER
(SHP.8), HARP SHAMROCK CREAM *(SHP.15)*, SHAMROCK
HONEY POT *(SHA.36)*

[Above left]

First row SHAMROCK PLATES, 8″ and 10″ *(SHA.29/30)*,
SHAMROCK PLATTERS, small and large *(SHA.44/45)*

Second row SHAMROCK COVERED TUREEN, ladle and plate
(SHA.42), SHAMROCK COFFEE CUP AND SAUCER *(SHA.10)*,
SHAMROCK COVERED VEGETABLE DISH *(SHA.46)*,
SHAMROCK BOUILLON CUP AND SAUCER *(SHA.41)*, GRAVY
BOAT *(SHA.60)*

[Above]

All Limpet

First row PLATE 7″ *(TLI.28)*, MILK JUG *(TLI.18)*, BREAD PLATE *(TLI.26)*, TEAPOT, large *(TLI.2)*, COFFEE POT *(TLI.7)*
Second row SLOP *(TLI.24)*, CREAM, small *(TLI.15)*, COVERED SUGAR *(TLI.22)*, SHELL SALT *(TLI.51)*
Third row COFFEE CUP AND SAUCER *(TLI.10)*, CUP AND SAUCER *(TLI.8)*, MUFFIN DISH *(TLI.35)*

[Opposite, bottom]

All Tridacna

First row PLATE 5″ *(TTR.28)*, BREAD PLATE *(TTR.26)*
Second row KETTLE *(TTR.6)*, COFFEE POT *(TTR.7)*, TEAPOT *(TTR.4)*, MILK JUG *(TTR.17)*, SLOP *(TTR.24)*
Third row BUTTER PLATE *(TTR.32)*, COFFEE CUP AND SAUCER *(TTR.10)*, SUGAR *(TTR.22)*, CUP AND SAUCER *(TTR.8)*, PEPPER SHAKER *(TTR.51)*, CREAM *(TTR.16)*, OPEN SALT *(TTR.50)*, MUSTARD *(TTR.49)*

[Above]

All Celtic Ring-Handle

First row SIDE PLATE *(TCE.27)*, BREAD PLATE *(TCE.26)*
Second row SLOP *(TCE.24)*, TEAPOT *(TCE.3)*, COFFEE POT *(TCE.7)*, KETTLE *(TCE.5)*, OPEN VEGETABLE DISH *(TCE.46)*
Third row CUP AND SAUCER *(TCE.8)*, COVERED SUGAR *(TCE.22)*, BREAKFAST CUP AND SAUCER *(TCE.11)*, CREAM *(TCE.15)*, COFFEE CUP AND SAUCER *(TCE.10)*

[Top]
All Celtic
First row SIDE PLATE (*TCL.27*), BREAD PLATE (*TCL.26*)
Second row SLOP (*TCL.24*), TEAPOT (*TCL.3*), COVERED HONEY
POT (*TCL.36*)
Third row COVERED SUGAR (*TCL.22*), CUP AND SAUCER
(*TCL.8*), CREAM (*TCL.15*)

[Right]
First row IVY SIDE PLATE (*TIV.27*), IVY BREAD PLATE
(*TIV.26*), CELTIC TALL BREAD PLATE (*TCT.26*), CELTIC TALL
SIDE PLATE (*TCT.27*)
Second row IVY SLOP (*TIV.24*), IVY TEAPOT (*TIV.3*), CELTIC
TALL TEAPOT (*TCT.3*), CELTIC TALL SLOP (*TCT.24*)
Third row IVY COVERED SUGAR (*TIV.23*), IVY CUP AND
SAUCER (*TIV.8*), IVY CREAM (*TIV.15*), CELTIC TALL SUGAR
(*TCT.20*), CELTIC TALL CUP AND SAUCER (*TCT.8*), CELTIC
TALL CREAM (*TCT.16*)

[Bottom right]
All Mask
First row COFFEE POT (*TMA.7*), SIDE PLATE (*TMA.27*), PLATE
5″ (*TMA.28*), BREAD PLATE (*TMA.26*), PLATE 7″ (*TMA.30*),
PLATE 6″ (*TMA.29*), MILK JUG (*TMA.19*)
Second row COVERED SUGAR, small (*TMA.22*), CREAM, small
(*TMA.15*), CREAM, large (*TMA.16*), SANDWICH TRAY
(*TMA.64*), SUGAR OPEN, large (*TMA.21*), TEAPOT (*TMA.2*)
Third row POWDER BOWL, small (*TMA.71*), SUGAR OPEN, small
(*TMA.20*), COFFEE CUP AND SAUCER (*TMA.10*), COVERED
BOX (*TMA.72*), CUP AND SAUCER (*TMA.8*), COVER SUGAR
(*TMA.23*), POWDER BOWL, large (*TMA.70*)

[Above]

First row IRISH POTS (VS. 140–VS. 143), IRISH POT JUG AND
SUGAR (JU. 53) With and without Shamrock decoration
Second row SHAMROCK GAELIC COFFEE CUP (SHA. 43), ROPE-
HANDLE MUG (TM. 40), GRASS MUG (TGR. 13), THORN MUG
(TTO. 13), LILY JUG AND SUGAR (JU. 56), TOY SHAMROCK
SUGAR AND JUG (JU. 79), CLEARY MUG (TM. 38), SHAMROCK
MUG, small (SHA. 57), medium (SHA. 56), large (SHA. 14)
Third row DOUBLE SHELL CREAM AND SUGAR (JU. 33), LILY
CREAM AND SUGAR (JU. 56), TOY SHELL CREAM AND SUGAR
(JU. 81), MASK MILK JUG (TMA. 19), RIBBON SUGAR AND
CREAM (JU. 68), IVY SUGAR, small (TIV. 20), IVY CREAM,
medium (TIV. 18), IVY SUGAR, large (TIV. 21), CREAM, large
(TIV. 17)
Fourth row BUTTER TUB, large (TM. 11), medium (TM. 13), small
(TM. 14), INDIVIDUAL SUGAR (TM. 22), SWAN, small (MI. 56),
INDIVIDUAL BUTTER (TM. 21), SWAN, large (MI. 55),
SHAMROCK BUTTER TUB, small (SHA. 67), medium (SHA. 66),
SHAMROCK COVERED BUTTER TUB (SHA. 34)

[Above]

First row LEAF PLATES (MI. 84–MI. 88), ERNE LEAF PLATE,
medium (MI. 77), large (MI. 76)
Second row HEART PLATES (MI. 81–MI. 83), PRIMROSE PLATE
(MI. 100), SHELL BUTTER PLATE (TM. 10), SYCAMORE
PLATES (MI. 106–109)
Third row FAN TUMBLER (TFA. 57–TFA. 63), WINE TUMBLER
(TM. 77–TM. 79), TUMBLERS (TM. 70–TM. 76)

[Above]

First row NILE VASE *(VS.168–VS.170)*, CORAL AND SHELL VASE *(VS.60)*, ERNE JUG *(JU.36)*, BAMBOO VASE *(VS.9)*, ULSTER VASE *(VS.153)*

Second row OCTAGONAL FLOWER POT, medium, small *(FP.35–36)*, CONE VASE, medium, small *(VS.58–59)*, NICKEL FLOWER POT *(FP.33)*, SHELL SLOP *(TSH.24)*, DIAMOND FLOWER POT *(FP.18)*, BELLEEK FLOWER POT, unflowered *(FP.7, 10, 11)*

Third row BOAT CREAM AND SUGAR *(JU.25)*, UNDINE CREAM *(JU.87)*, BOAT ASH TRAY *(TM.1)*, FERMANAGH VASE *(VS.94)*, LIFFORD JUG *(JU.54)*, SEAHORSE FLOWER HOLDER *(VS.206)*, PIG, large, small *(MI.53–54)*, ACORN CRATE *(MI.10)*

Fourth row CLEARY JUG AND SUGAR *(JU.28)*, LOW LILY JUG AND SUGAR *(JU.56)*, TRIDACNA EGG CUP *(TTR.48)*, SHAMROCK ROUND BOX *(SHA.77)*, SHAMROCK EGG CUP *(SHA.48)*, DAIRY SUGAR AND CREAM *(JU.30)*, SCALE JUG *(JU.72)*, SHAMROCK TRINKET BOX OVAL *(SHA.72)*, TOY SHELL JUG AND SUGAR, small *(JU.80)*, RATHMORE JUG *(JU.66)*

[Above]

First row SUNFLOWER VASE *(VS.222)*, SHAMROCK TYPHA JUG *(JU.86)*, IRISH HARP, large *(MI.44)*, IRISH HARP, small *(MI.45)*, HARP VASE *(VS.125)*, DAISY VASE *(VS.65)*, SHAMROCK TRUNK STUMP VASE *(SHA.83)*, PANEL VASE, small *(VS.175)*, large *(VS.174)*, ISLAND VASE *(VS.146)*, SHAMROCK PIERCED VASE *(SHA.88)*

Second row FEATHER VASE, small *(VS.93)*, large *(VS.92)*, MARINE VASE, small *(VS.160)*, large *(VS.159)*, ROCK SPILL, large *(VS.194)*, medium *(VS.195)*, small *(VS.196)*

Third row RATHMORE FLOWER POT, unfooted *(FP.47)*, LILY SPILL, large *(VS.154)*, MOOR VASE *(VS.163)*, DOLPHIN SPILL *(VS.77)*, SHAMROCK SPILL *(SHA.87)*, FINNER FLOWER POT *(FP.24)*

[Above]

All Celtic

First row ARRAN MOR VASE, small *(TCE.82)*, TARA VASE
(TCE.92), VASE K *(TCE.94)*, ROSE BOWL CENTRE *(TCE.95)*
Second row DIAMOND VASE *(VS.66)*, CELTIC VASE J *(TCE.93)*,
CELTIC SPILL R *(TCE.91)*, CELTIC FRUIT DISH *(TCE.31)*
Third row CELTIC LIFFEY VASE *(TCE.86)*, CELTIC CYLINDER
SPILL *(TCE.83)*, CELTIC TOY CREAM AND SUGAR, CELTIC
SALAD BOWL AND STAND *(TCE.47)*, CELTIC POT CREAM
AND SUGAR
Fourth row CELTIC RINGED SPILL *(TCE.85)*, CELTIC SPILL E
(TCE.89), CELTIC SPILL A *(TCE.87)*, CELTIC SPILL C
(TCE.88), CELTIC CREAM *(TCE.15)*, LEPRECHAUN *(MI.50)*,
CELTIC SUGAR *(TCE.20)*, CELTIC SPILL H *(TCE.90)*, CELTIC
ASHTRAY *(TCE.78)*, SAINT SPILL *(VS.203)*

[Top right]

First row BLESSED VIRGIN MARY, large *(HO.8)*, ANGEL FONT,
large *(HO.2)*, CELTIC CROSS FONT *(HO.10)*, ANGEL FONT
KNEELING, large *(HO.4)*, SACRED HEART STATUE, large
(HO.19)
Second row ANGEL FONT, small *(HO.3)*, CORAL AND SHELL
WALL BRACKET *(FP.60)*, ANGEL FONT KNEELING, small
(HO.5), CELTIC FONT NO 6 *(HO.12)*
Third row CHERUB FONT, large *(HO.13)*, SACRED HEART
FONT NO 8 *(HO.21)*, SACRED HEART FONT NO 4 *(HO.22)*,
CELTIC FONT NO 5 *(HO.11)*, CORAL AND SHELL FONT
(HO.15), FONT NO 10 *(HO.18)*, ANGEL FONT HANGING
(HO.1)

[Above]

First row TRIPLE CARDIUM *(VS.41–44)*
Second row DOLPHIN AND SHELL *(VS.75)*, CARDIUM ON CORAL
(VS.40–VS.37), CORAL AND SHELL VASE *(VS.60)*
Third row TRIPLE SPILL, large *(VS.233)*, CARDIUM ON SHELL
(VS.33–VS.36), VICTORIA SHELL *(VS.255)*

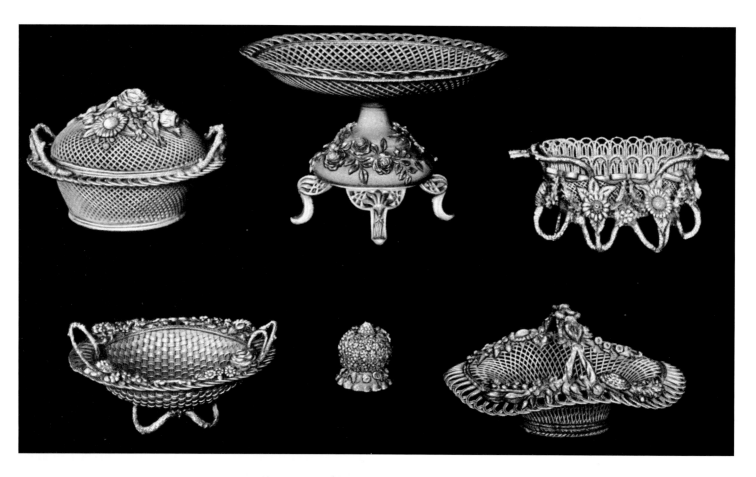

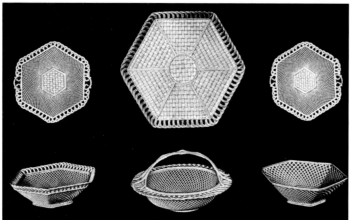

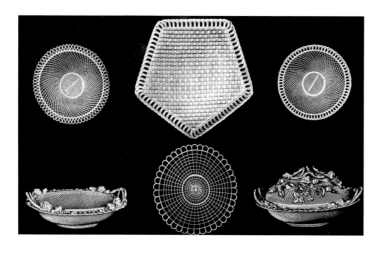

[Above]

First row ROUND COVERED BASKET large *(BS.62)*, FLOWERED WOVEN COMPORT *(DS.43)*, RATHMORE BASKET *(BS.54)*

Second row ROUND BASKET NO 8 *(BS.41)*, TRINKET BOX *(MI.21)*, HENSHALL'S TWIG, large *(BS.25)*

[Top left]

First row HEXAGON CAKE PLATE, with handles *(BS.34)*, HEXAGON WOVEN TRAY *(BS.82)*

Second row HEXAGON WOVEN FRUIT BASKET *(BS.35)*, ROUND UNFLOWERED BASKET, centre handle *(BS.65)*, HEXAGON FLAT ROAD A J BASKET, no loops *(BS.32)*

[Bottom left]

First row SPECIAL CAKE PLATE, unhandled *(BS.10)*, PENTAGONAL TRAY *(BS.81)*, CAKE PLATE ROUND ROD *(BS.11)*

Second row OVAL BASKET UNCOVERED, large *(BS.44)*, SPIDER WEB PLATE *(BS.74)*, OVAL COVERED BASKET, large *(BS.42)*

Acknowledgements

My interest in and appreciation of Belleek dates back to the late 1950s, when I came over and settled in Ireland from my home in East Africa, but it wasn't until I moved to London and started dealing in antiques that I really became engrossed in the subject. Then in 1986 I was fortunate enough to spend some days with Horace Manning Man in Houston, Texas, photographing and cataloguing his extensive collection. From this grew the ambition to publish a book and share my enthusiasm with others. Of course, forming the idea was easy; putting it into practice was another matter and for that I am immensely indebted to my friend Edward Bramah who gave me the encouragement and advice I needed to get the project started.

My vision for the book was that it should principally consist of good colour photographs to help collectors identify pieces they had or hoped to acquire. Getting together the photographs was therefore my main task and I really do owe my sincere thanks to the very many people who helped me achieve my goal:

Mrs McElroy, her sister Gladys Hall, and her daughter Olga who allowed me to turn their house upside-down for three days while we photographed their beautiful collection.

To all those warm-hearted and generous Americans who not only let me photograph their collections but, often on more than one occasion, opened their houses to me, guided, fetched, carried, entertained, and generally hosted me in every way they could.

Susan and Jack Bernstein in Portland, Oregon.

Kermit Rosen in Seattle, Washington who took me to meet Del Domke who supplied me with so many transparencies. Betty and Don Clinton in Los Angeles, who drove over two hundred miles taking me to see Chuck and Andy Oster, Ruby and Bedell Dickinson, Irwine and Maxine Steinberg, and Evelyn and Bill Twiss.

Fred Gary in San Diego, California, who introduced me to Lilian Rosebaum and Frances Horton.

Margaret Powers, her daughter Nancy, and son-in-law Larry, in Chicago, who let me use their house like an hotel, dropping in whenever I needed a base to operate from. Margaret and her friend Bob McCarthy, took me to the Birks Museum, Decatur, where I met Mary Turner, the director of the Museum.

Josephine Corriveau and Janet in Manchester, New Hampshire. Edie Jacobson in New York.

Dr Robert Gregg in Boulder, Colorado.

Gene and Susan Krach in Glen Ann, Maryland.

My friends in the UK Belleek Collectors Group.

Jan Golaszewski, the chairman, who endlessly advised, encouraged and arranged on my behalf.

Graham and Maureen Munton, Roy Holihead and Fiona and Charles Easthope who allowed me to take away their precious pieces to be shot in a studio.

Christine and Peter McCormack who had their collection specially photographed for me.

Eddie Renshaw who not only shot his own pieces for me but did Beverly Poole's and Chris Marvel's as well.

Margaret and Rodney Capper: Rodney drove miles to the photographers so that I could have their pieces photographed.

Pat Campbell's widow Doris, who let me photograph Pat's extensive collection before it was put away following his untimely death.

My dear friend Walter Gruber, who sadly is also no longer here to see this book but who laid the ground for me to meet Mairead Dunlevy of the National Museum of Ireland. Mairead not only provided the photographs that I needed but arranged for the Ceramics Department to be specially opened for me.

Michael Robinson of the Ulster Museum in Belfast who also provided photographs of the museum's pieces. In fact Michael can take credit for much of my passion for Belleek since it was he who many years before had advised me to visit Horace Man.

Photographers Gerald Wells of Northern Counties Photographers, Stoke-on-Trent. Harry and Lenni Brown-Reid of Studio 3, Ballinamallard.

Dr Patrick Doran of the University of Limerick for letting me have the excellent photograph of the wonderful 'Stags Head' candelabra in their possession.

My husband Jim who, apart from spending endless hours cataloguing, checking and sorting out the photographs on the computer, drove me all over Ireland and took photographs for me at the Pottery and photographed Murray and Eunice Robinson's fine pieces.

Of course, taking the photographs was only one part of the exercise. Little could have been achieved without the co-operation and support of Belleek. First Martina Kerr Bromley who had been such a staunch ally in forming the UK Collectors Group and who now helped out again, giving me contacts and introductions world-wide. Then there were the management and staff at the Pottery itself: Fergus Cleary with his fund of knowledge of the history and workings of Belleek; Patricia McCauley who patiently dug out information and dealt with all my queries and requests. Finally I would like to thank George Moore, the owner of the Pottery. Hardly was the ink dry on his purchase agreement than I was knocking on his door, looking for support. George, who with his wife Angela showed me great kindness and hospitality at their home in San Diego, has given me encouragement throughout the development of this book. I am most grateful to him for contributing the foreword on where Belleek is today and where it is going tomorrow.

I have had great fun in producing this book. I have made many friends and look back fondly on many memories – being put up in Betty and Don Clinton's charming Japanese-style guest house; meeting so many of the Los Angeles Chapter of the Belleek Collectors Society, both at the home of Evelyn and Bill Twiss and then at one of their regular meetings (I was delighted to be given a copy of the LA Chapter's book *Belleek* to add to my library); being shown Bob Gregg's amazing collection of ants, butterflies and moths. No wonder he is affectionately known as 'the bog man'. Gene Krach introduced me to a snake farm and then followed it up with a visit to a 'stately home', American-style, and some wonderful formal gardens and glass-houses. Undertaking the photography was also a memorable experience. I had half an hour's patient instruction from Chris Jarvis (of Executive Cameras in London) before he crossed his fingers, hired me a Hassleblad, and sent me on my way around the world. For the most part I managed to cope quite well, but I won't forget Josephine Corriveau and I struggling to overcome the triple hazards of snow, wind, and cold to obtain the shots of her pieces. Nor will I forget the disappointment of shooting two rolls of film at Lilian Rosebaum's, only to discover later that the film had not been winding on.

Now all of that is over. I hope you enjoy this book and that it enables you to share some of the pleasure that I have gained from this beautiful and crafted porcelain that is Belleek.

Marion Langham
October, 1992

Bibliography

Richard K Degenhardt, *Belleek, The Complete Collector's Guide and Illustrated Reference.* 1978
Los Angeles Chapter of the Belleek Collector's Society, *Belleek.* 1990.
John B Cunningham, *The Story of Belleek*, 1992.
S McCrum, *The Belleek Pottery, Ulster Museum.*
National Museum of Ireland, *Early Belleek Wares*, 1978
Horace Manning Man, *Inventory of an Irish Belleek Collection*, 1987.

Peadar Livingstone, *The Fermanagh Story*, 1969.
Photograph album belonging to R W Armstrong, now in the National Museum, Kildare Street, Dublin.
Michael Berthoud, *A Compendium of British Cups*, 1990.
Nicholas Pine, *The Concise Encyclopaedia and Price Guide to Goss China*, 1989.
Richard Dennis, *The Parian Phenomenon*, 1989.
Wolf Mankowitz and Reginald G Hagger, *The Concise Encyclopedia of English Pottery and Porcelain*, 1968.

Index

Rarity within each category is indicated by letter code A-D with
A the rarest. Items not illustrated are indicated 'n.i.'.